Children's Pr

Compiled by

GREG LEAVERS AND PHIL BURT

Marshall Pickering
An Imprint of HarperCollins*Publishers*

First published in Great Britain in 1991 by Marshall Pickering
Marshall Pickering is an imprint of
HarperCollins*Religious*
Part of HarperCollins *Publishers*
77–85 Fulham Palace Road, London W6 8JB

Compilation Copyright © 1991 Greg Leavers, Phil Burt & Peter Horrobin

The Compilers assert the moral right to be identified as the compilers of this work

Printed and bound in Great Britain by HarperCollins Manufacturing, Glasgow

A catalogue record for this book is available from the British Library

ISBN: 0-551-02423-2

Contents

Preface

Children's Praise is the newest book in the *Mission Praise* series of song-books. It is actually designed to complement *Junior Praise*, which has been tremendously popular since its publication in 1986, selling more than one million copies. *Junior Praise* was for older children – middle primary and upwards. *Children's Praise* is for the younger ones.

The songs in *Children's Praise* are a mixture of old favourites and previously unpublished items. They should be easy and fun to learn. They are arranged for the main part alphabetically, although we have tried to avoid page turns in the middle of items. There is a full subject index at the back of the book.

We would strongly encourage instrumental involvement by the children. Each song accordingly has a clear melody line that can be followed by recorders, flutes and the like. Guitar chords have been supplied with capo chord options. These can be used equally with the automatic chord facility on many electronic keyboards.

We hope and pray that children will be helped by this book to know how special they are to God, and how they may know and serve him with joy in their everyday lives.

GREG LEAVERS, PHIL BURT AND PETER HORROBIN

1 All the children need the Saviour

Marjorie A. Anderson

Ellen R. Thompson

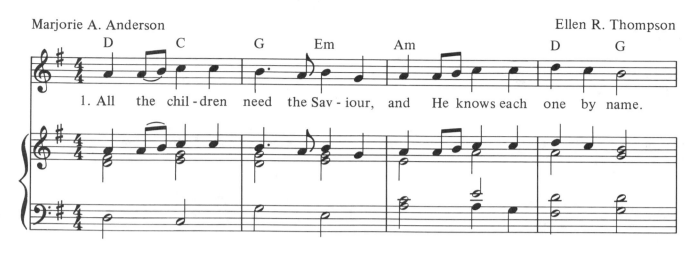

1 All the children need the Saviour,
and He knows each one by name.
Every child is dear to Jesus,
and He loves each one the same.

2 Some one needs to tell the children,
or they'll never, never know
Jesus came to earth to save them,
He's our Friend who loves us so.

2 Alleluia, alleluia, give thanks

Don Fishel
arr. Norman Warren

Capo 3

Alleluia, alleluia, give thanks to the risen Lord!
Alleluia, alleluia, give praise to His name.

1 Jesus is Lord of all the earth.
  He is the king of creation.
    Alleluia, alleluia . . .

2 Spread the good news through all the earth,
  Jesus has died and has risen.
    Alleluia, alleluia . . .

3 Come let us praise the living God,
  joyfully sing to our Saviour!
    Alleluia, alleluia . . .

3 All things bright and beautiful

All things bright and beautiful,
all creatures great and small,
all things wise and wonderful,
the Lord God made them all.

1 Each little flower that opens,
  each little bird that sings,
  He made their glowing colours,
  He made their tiny wings.
  All things bright. . .

2 The purple-headed mountain,
  the river running by,
  the sunset, and the morning
  that brightens up the sky;
  All things bright. . .

3 The cold wind in the winter,
  the pleasant summer sun,
  the ripe fruits in the garden,
  He made them every one.
  All things bright. . .

4 He gave us eyes to see them,
  and lips that we might tell
  how great is God almighty,
  who has made all things well.
  All things bright. . .

4 All things were made by God

Mary Le Barr alt.

Ellen R. Thompson

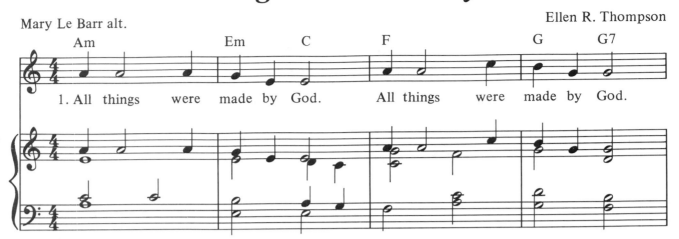

1. All things were made by God. All things were made by God.

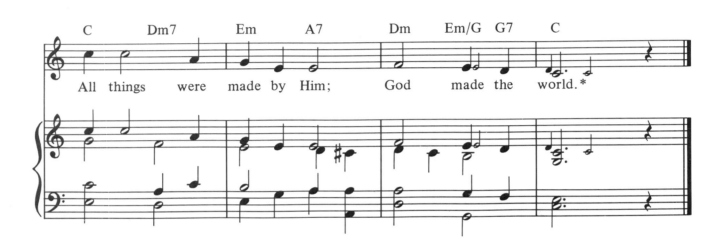

All things were made by Him; God made the world.*

1 All things were made by God.
   All things were made by God.
   All things were made by Him;
   God made the world.*

2 Come, let us sing our thanks.
   Come, let us sing our thanks.
   Come, let us sing our thanks;
   sing thanks to God.

* Sun, moon, land, sea, sky, trees, birds, our bread, our food, our friends, etc.
The smaller notes may be used for: mothers, fathers, brothers, sisters, babies, flowers, etc.

5 And God said

J.B. Wood
Capo 1

J.W. Wood

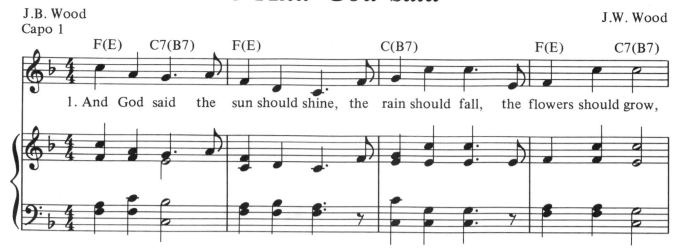

1. And God said the sun should shine, the rain should fall, the flowers should grow,

and God said the birds should sing and it was so, was so.

1 And God said the sun should shine,
   the rain should fall, the flowers should grow,
   and God said the birds should sing,
   and it was so, was so.

2 And God said the grass should grow,
   the trees bear fruit, the winds should blow,
   and God said the streams should flow,
   and it was so, was so.

6 Anytime, anywhere

Barbara Ryberg
Capo 2

Ruth Brabazon
arr. Ellen R. Thompson

Anytime, anywhere I can talk to God.
When I'm glad, when I'm sad, I can talk to God.
Sometimes on my knees I pray. Sometimes as I work or play,
when I need Him through the day, He is my best friend.

7 Away in a manger

W.J. Kilpatrick

Capo 3

1 Away in a manger, no crib for a bed,
   the little Lord Jesus laid down His sweet head.
   The stars in the bright sky looked down where He lay,
   the little Lord Jesus asleep in the hay.

2 The cattle are lowing, the Baby awakes,
   but little Lord Jesus, no crying He makes.
   I love You Lord Jesus! Look down from the sky,
   and stay by my side until morning is nigh.

3 Be near me, Lord Jesus; I ask You to stay
   close by me for ever and love me, I pray.
   Bless all the dear children in Your tender care,
   and fit us for heaven to live with You there.

8 Be kind

P. Dowman

Capo 3

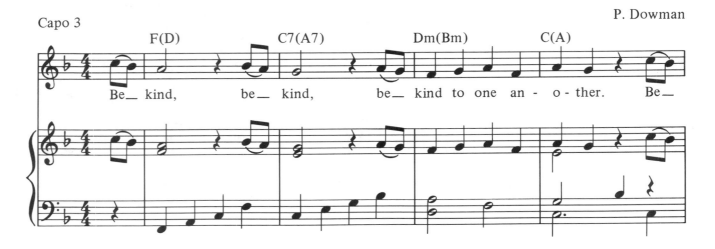

Be— kind, be— kind, be— kind to one an - o - ther. Be—

kind, be— kind, be kind to one an - o - ther.

Be kind, be kind, be kind to one another.
Be kind, be kind, be kind to one another.

9 Believe on the Lord Jesus Christ

Avis B. Christiansen

Harry D. Clarke

Capo 1

Be - lieve on the Lord Je - sus Christ, be -
lieve on the Lord Je - sus Christ, be - lieve on the
Lord Je - sus Christ, and you shall be saved.

Believe on the Lord Jesus Christ,
believe on the Lord Jesus Christ,
believe on the Lord Jesus Christ,
and you shall be saved.

10 Boisterous buzzing

Winifred Elliott
Arr. Johnnel Park
and Ellen R. Thompson

1. Bois-t'rous, buz-zing, bark-ing things, with paws and legs and claws and wings;

all that swims or crawls or sings; or flaps or flops or flips or flings:

our Cre - a - tor made all these, and big and lit - tle you's and me's.

big and lit - tle you's and me's.

1 Boisterous, buzzing, barking things,
with paws and legs and claws and wings,
all that swims or crawls or sings;
or flaps or flops or flips or flings:
our Creator made all these,
and big and little you's and me's.

2 Bugs and birds and bears and bees;
and buds that burst on blossoming trees;
fluffy clouds before the breeze;
and stars and skies and streams and seas:
our Creator made all these,
and big and little you's and me's.

3 Girls and boys and Mum and Dad,
the kind and good, or even bad—
all who please and make Him glad,
and even those who make Him sad:
our Creator made all these,
and big and little you's and me's.

11 Build a boat

Doris I. Black
arr. Phil Burt

Capo 1

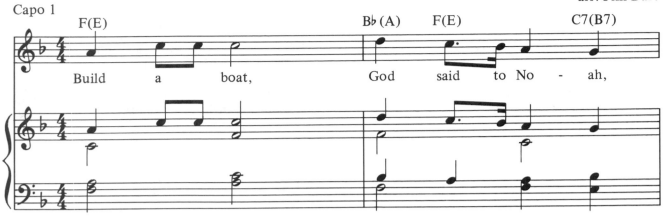

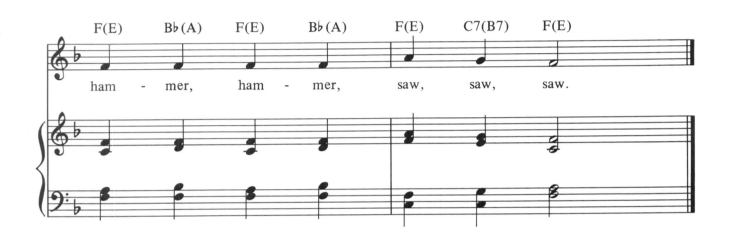

1 Build a boat, God said to Noah,
   hammer, hammer, saw, saw, saw.

2 Go in the boat, God said to Noah,
   step, step, step, step, step, step.

3 The rain came down, came down, came down,
   pitter pat, pitter pat.

4 The sun came out, came out, came out,
   shine, shine, shine, shine, shine, shine.

5 Go out of the boat, God said to Noah,
   step, step, step, step, step, step.

6 Thank You, God, thank You, God,
   pray, pray, pray, pray, pray, pray.

12 *Care for one another*

Betty A. Riley

Care for one another.
Care for one another.
Care for the old,
care for the young.
Care for the sick,
and care for your friend.
Care for one another,
care for one another.
For God's Word says
'Care for one another'.

13 Come and praise

Anon

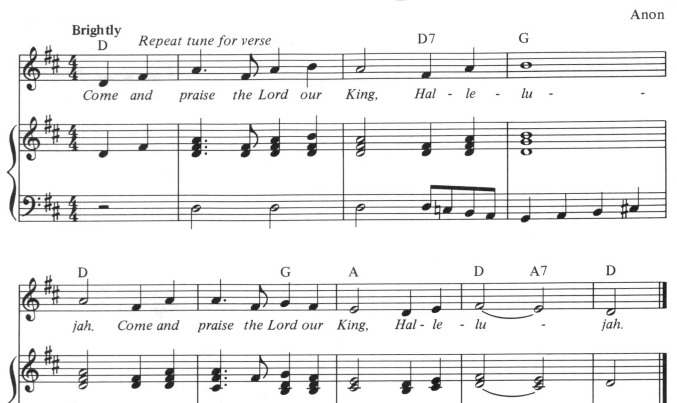

Come and praise the Lord our King, Hallelujah.
Come and praise the Lord our King, Hallelujah.

1 Christ was born in Bethlehem, Hallelujah;
  Son of God and Son of Man, Hallelujah.
     Come and praise . . .

2 From Him love and wisdom came, Hallelujah;
  all His life was free from blame, Hallelujah.
     Come and praise . . .

3 Jesus died at Calvary, Hallelujah;
  rose again triumphantly, Hallelujah.
     Come and praise . . .

4 He will cleanse us from our sin, Hallelujah,
  if we live by faith in Him, Hallelujah.
     Come and praise . . .

5 He will be with us today, Hallelujah,
  and forever with us stay, Hallelujah.
     Come and praise . . .

6 We will live with Him one day, Hallelujah,
  and for ever with Him stay, Hallelujah.
     Come and praise . . .

14 Come into His presence

Anon
arr. Phil Burt

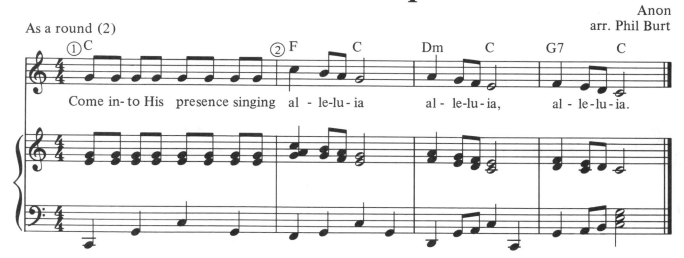

As a round (2)

Come in-to His presence singing al - le-lu - ia   al - le-lu - ia,   al - le-lu - ia.

1   Come into His presence singing, alleluia, alleluia, alleluia

2   Come into His presence singing, Jesus is Lord, Jesus is Lord, Jesus is Lord

3   Come into His presence singing, glory to God, glory to God, glory to God

15 Come on girls and boys

Greg Leavers
arr. Phil Burt

Come on girls and boys, put a way your toys, find a space to dance and sing and make a joy-ful noise, we're going to shout GOOD NEWS FOR EV'RY ONE. We're going to sing, The Sa-viour of the world is born, we're going to dance and sing as our prai-ses ring, our

thanks and love_ are the gifts we bring,_ to ce le brate the birth of a King.

to ce le brate the birth of a King. _

Come on girls and boys,
put away your toys,
find a space to dance and sing
and make a joyful noise,
we're going to shout

GOOD NEWS FOR EVERY ONE.
We're going to sing,
the Saviour of the world is born,
we're going to dance and sing
as our praises ring,
our thanks and love
are the gifts we bring,
to celebrate the birth of a King
to celebrate the birth of a King.

16 Come on and praise the Lord

S. & J. Doddridge

1. Come on and praise the Lord,_ come on and praise the Lord,_ come on and praise the Lord,_ I'm going to pra-ise the Lord._

1 Come on and praise the Lord,
  come on and praise the Lord,
  come on and praise the Lord,
  I'm going to praise the Lord.

2 Come on and clap your hands (clap clap clap clap)

3 Come on and stamp your feet (stamp stamp stamp stamp)

4 Come on and shout Amen (Amen)

5 Come on and raise your hands

6 Come on and turn around

7 Come on and dance with joy
  etc

17 *Choose you this day*

J.R. Willanger and
Ellen R. Thompson

Group 1	Choose you this day
Group 2	Choose you this day
Group 1	Whom you will serve
Group 2	Whom you will serve
Group 1 and 2	But as for me (for me)
	and my house (my house)
	we'll serve the Lord,
	we'll serve the Lord.

18 Daniel and his friends

Philip P. Bliss

Capo 1

1. Dan - iel and his friends must choose what is right or wrong.

Should they take the ea - sy way or fol - low God's com - mand?

Dare to be a Dan - iel! Dare to stand a - lone!

Dare to have a pur - pose firm!__ Dare to make it known.

1 Daniel and his friends must choose
  what is right or wrong.
  Should they take the easy way or
  follow God's command?
      Dare to be a Daniel! Dare to stand alone!
  Dare to have a purpose firm! Dare to make it known.

2 Three friends knew they should not bow,
  when the signal came.
  For they loved the Lord their God and
  would not worship man.
      Dare to be . . .

3 When you find that you must choose,
  do what's right and good.
  Think of Daniel and his friends and
  please the Lord your God.
      Dare to be . . .

19 Deep and wide

arr. Andy Silver

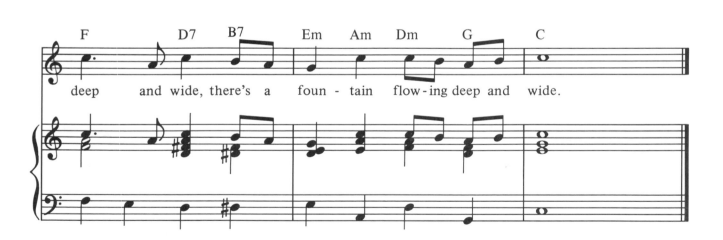

Deep and wide, deep and wide,
there's a fountain flowing deep and wide;
Deep and wide, deep and wide,
there's a fountain flowing deep and wide.

20 Every day we say

Marie H. Frost
arr. Phil Burt

Capo 1

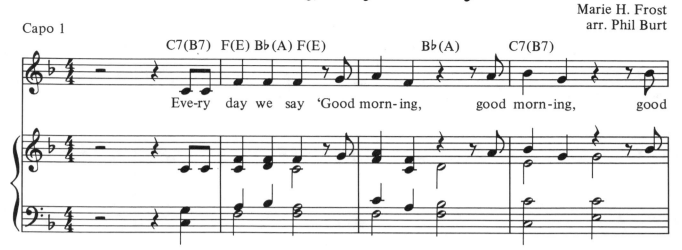

Eve-ry day we say 'Good morn-ing, good morn-ing, good

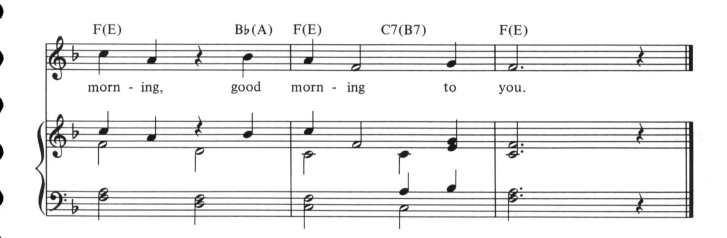

morn - ing, good morn - ing to you.

1 Every day we say 'Good morning, good morning,
good morning, good morning to you'.

2 Every day we say 'A welcome, a welcome,
a welcome, a welcome to you'.

3 Every day we say 'God loves you, God loves you,
God loves you, God loves you and me'.

21 Far beyond the Universe

Joan Robinson

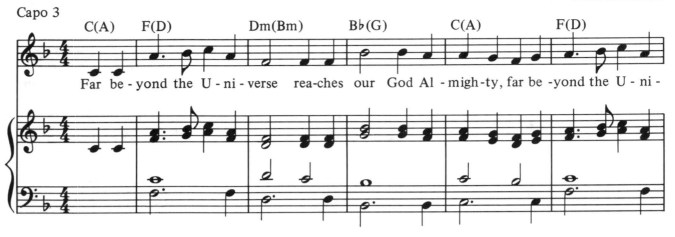

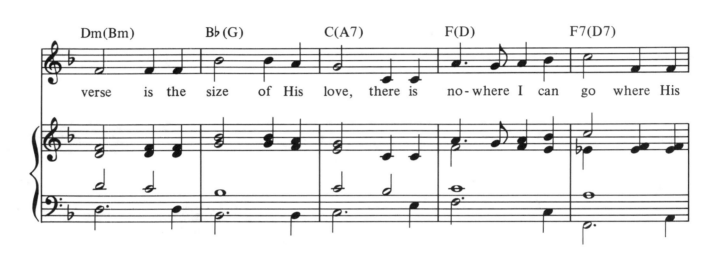

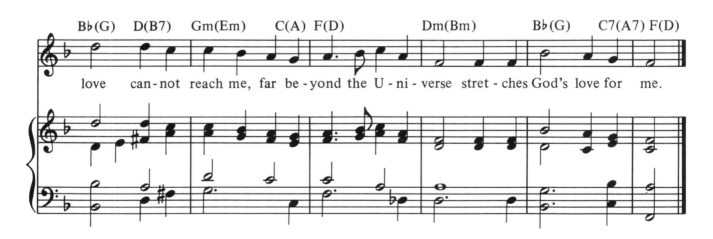

Far beyond the Universe reaches our God almighty,
far beyond the Universe is the size of His love,
there is nowhere I can go where His love cannot reach me,
far beyond the Universe stretches God's love for me.

22 Father be with her family

Greg Leavers
arr. Phil Burt

Capo 3

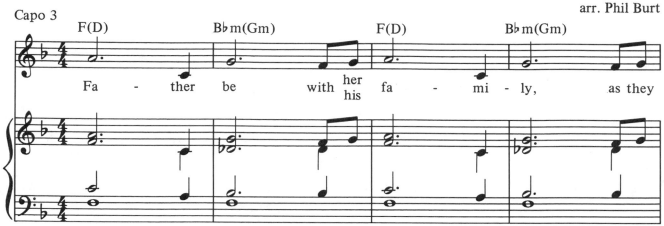

Fa - ther be with her/his fa - mi - ly, as they

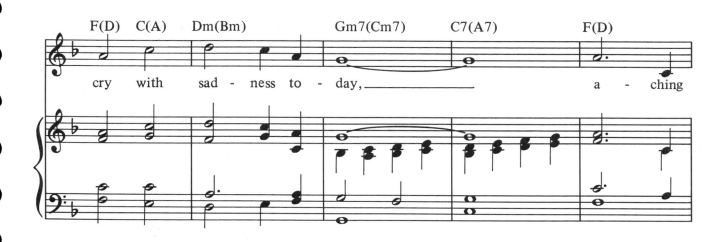

cry with sad - ness to - day, _____ a - ching

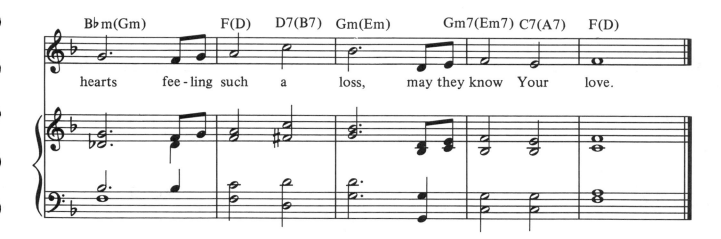

hearts fee-ling such a loss, may they know Your love.

1. Father be with *her/his/their family,
   as they cry with sadness today,
   aching hearts feeling such a loss;
   may they know Your love.

2. Comfort them with Your love, oh Lord,
   as they try to understand
   why You called *her/his/them to be with You;
   may they know Your peace.

* (Use the relevant word or use the child's name)

23 Father I'm so sorry

Greg Leavers
arr. Phil Burt

Fa - ther I'm so sor - ry, for naugh ty things I have done._____ Fa - ther please for - give me, for naugh ty things I have done._____ Thank you Lord for Your prom -

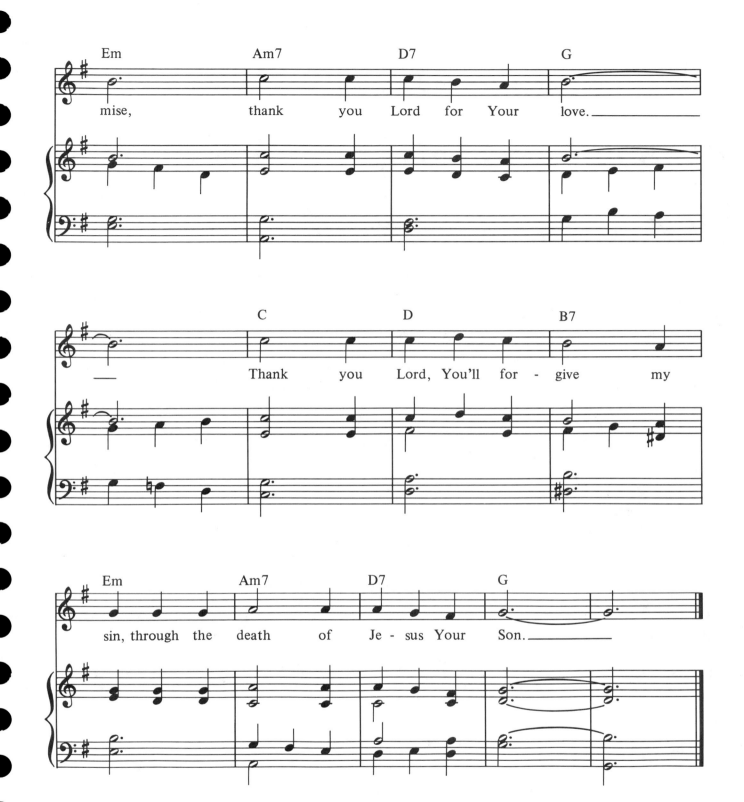

Father I'm so sorry, for naughty things I have done.
Father please forgive me, for naughty things I have done.
Thank You Lord for Your promise, thank You Lord for Your love.
Thank You Lord, You'll forgive my sin, through the death of Jesus Your Son.

24 First Thessalonians

Joan Baxendale

Linda Broyles

Capo 1

Words and Music First published by Standard Publishing / Copyright Control

This is what you ought to do, ___ 'You ought to please God'. ___

1 First Thessalonians four: one,
   is a very good verse for me;
   its message tells me what to do;
   it's a very good verse for you.
   'You ought to please God.
   You ought to please God'.
   This is what you ought to do,
   'You ought to please God'.

2 Ephesians four: thirty two,
   is a very good verse for me;
   its message tells me what to do;
   it's a very good verse for you.
   'Be kind to one another.
   Be kind to one another'.
   This is what you ought to do,
   'Be kind to one another'.

3 Oh, Luke ten: twenty seven,
   is a very good verse for me;
   its message tells me what to do;
   it's a very good verse for you.
   'Love the Lord your God.
   Love the Lord your God'.
   This is what you ought to do,
   'Love the Lord Your God'.

25 Father for our friends we pray

Greg Leavers
arr. Phil Burt

Capo 3

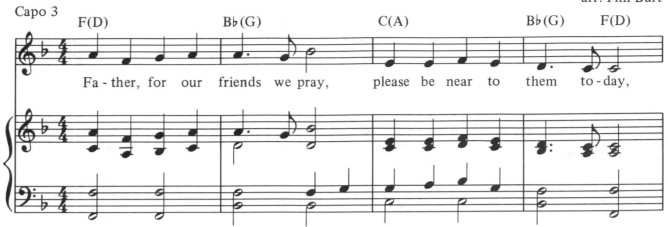

1 Father, for our friends we pray,
  please be near to them today,
  in their sadness, through their tears,
  may they know Your peace.

2 Now that he/she is by Your side
  comfort friends when they ask 'why'.
  Their dear loved one had to die,
  may they know Your love.

3 Though part of their lives has gone,
  give them strength to carry on,
  as they face the days to come,
  may they know Your care.

26 Fisherman Peter

1 Fisherman Peter on the sea,
   drop your net boy, and follow Me!
   Fisherman Peter on the sea,
   drop your net boy, and follow Me!

2 Rich young ruler, plain to see,
   can't love money and follow Me!   } twice

3 Lonely Zaccheus in the tree,
   love your neighbour and follow Me!   } twice

4 Nicodemus Pharisee,
   new life comes when you follow Me!   } twice

5 Doubting Thomas, from doubt be free,
   stop your doubting and follow Me!   } twice

27 Five little loaves

Lilian Waldecker

1 Hold up five fingers

2 Hold up two fingers

3 Palms up

4 Extend palms forward indicating giving

5 Clap

6 Hold up one finger

7 Point upward

8 Palms together—moving outward farther and farther

9 Large circular motion with both arms

① Five little loaves and

② two little fish was

③ all the little boy had,

④ but he gave it all to Jesus,
it made Jesus glad.

① Five little loaves,

② two little fish, just enough for

⑥ one.

⑦ Jesus made it

⑧ grow and grow 'til it fed every
(may also be spoken with expression)

⑨ one.

28 Five, four, three, two, one

Joan Robinson

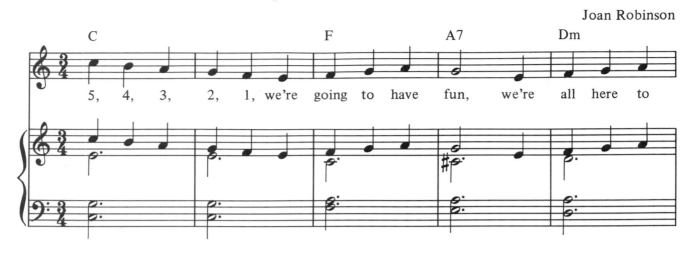

5, 4, 3, 2, 1, we're going to have fun, we're all here to

learn of Je - sus God's Son. . . 5, 4, 3, 2, 1, we're

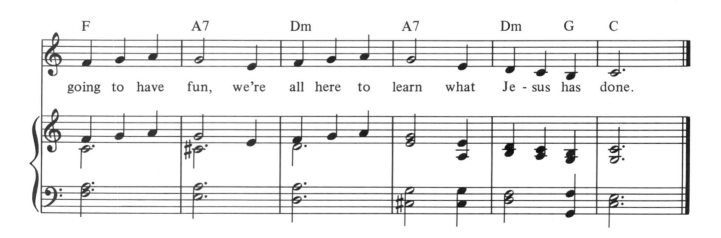

going to have fun, we're all here to learn what Je - sus has done.

5,4,3,2,1, we're going to have fun,
we're all here to learn of Jesus God's Son.
5,4,3,2,1, we're going to have fun,
we're all here to learn what Jesus has done.

29 Follow Me

Steve Kersys

Phil Burt

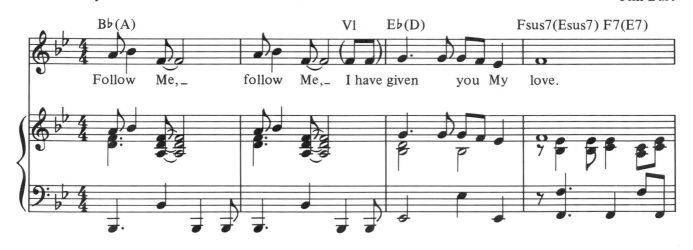

1 Follow Me, follow Me, I have given you My love.
   Follow Me, follow Me, I have given you My life.

2 Follow Me, follow Me, give your love to Me.
   Follow Me, follow Me, give your life to Me.

3 Follow Me, follow Me, tell others of My love.
   Follow Me, follow Me, tell others of My life.

30 For the sun, we thank You

Sylvia Tester
arr. Phil Burt

Capo 3

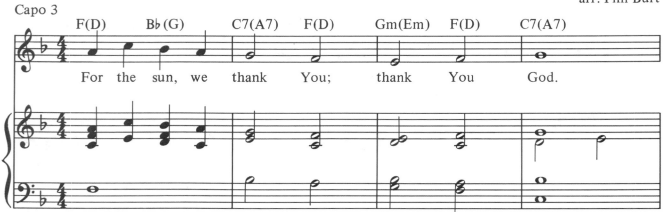

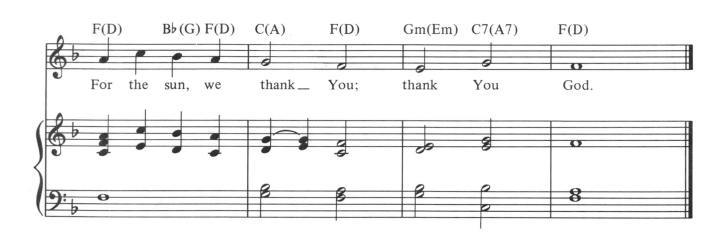

For the sun, we thank You;
thank You God.
For the sun, we thank You;
thank You God.

31 Forgive me, God

Capo 3

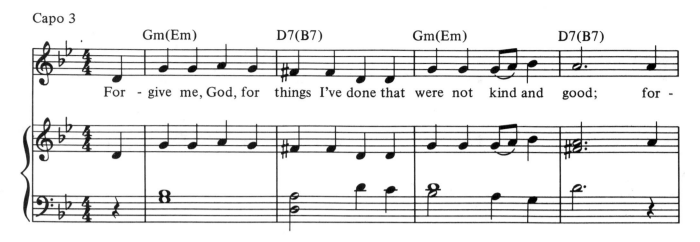

For - give me, God, for things I've done that were not kind and good; for -

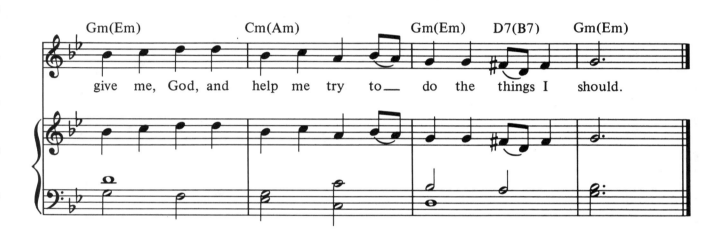

give me, God, and help me try to__ do the things I should.

Forgive me, God, for things I've done
that were not kind and good;
forgive me, God, and help me try
to do the things I should.

'Forgive Me God' from 'Sing for Joy', compiled and edited by Norman and Margarel Healey, © 1961, by The Seabury Press, Inc., Reprinted by permission of Harper Colling Publishers USA

32 From my knees to my nose

Greg Leavers
arr. Phil Burt

Capo 3

From my knees to my nose,_ from my head to my toes,_ does God,_____ know all a - bout me if I'm ha ppy or sad,_ If I'm good or I'm bad,_ does God _____ know all a - bout me? The an swer is yes_____ and He

From my knees to my nose,
from my head to my toes,
does God know all about me?
If I'm happy or sad,
if I'm good or I'm bad,
does God know all about me?
The answer is yes
and He loves me the best,
though He knows everything about me?
The answer is yes
and He loves me the best,
and He knows that my name is . . . *(Shout name)*

33 Give me oil in my lamp

Traditional

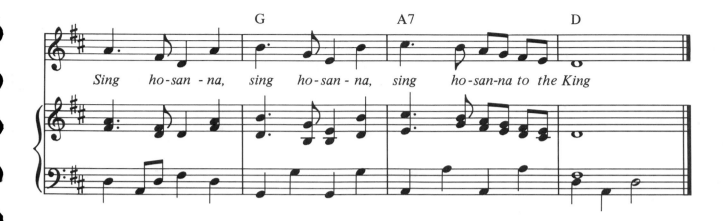

G   A7   D

Sing   ho-san - na,   sing   ho-san - na,   sing   ho-san-na to the King

1 Give me oil in my lamp, keep me burning.
   Give me oil in my lamp, I pray.
   Give me oil in my lamp, keep me burning,
   keep me burning till the break of day.

   Sing hosanna, sing hosanna,
   sing hosanna to the King of Kings!
   Sing hosanna, sing hosanna,
   sing hosanna to the King!

2 Give me joy in my heart, keep me singing.
   Give me joy in my heart, I pray.
   Give me joy in my heart, keep me singing,
   keep me singing till the break of day.
      Sing hosanna . . .

3 Give me love in my heart, keep me serving.
   Give me love in my heart, I pray.
   Give me love in my heart, keep me serving,
   keep me serving till the break of day.
      Sing hosanna . . .

4 Give me peace in my heart, keep me resting.
   Give me peace in my heart, I pray.
   Give me peace in my heart, keep me resting.
   keep me resting till the break of day.
      Sing hosanna . . .

34 God created all the earth

Anon
arr. Greg Leavers

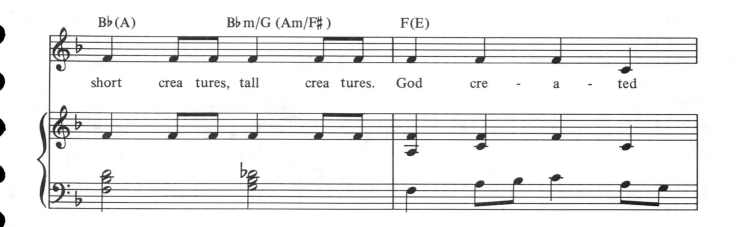

short crea tures, tall crea tures. God cre - a - ted

all the earth, I know, I know, I know.

God created all the earth,
I know, I know, I know,
God created all the earth,
I know, I know, I know.
There were fat creatures, thin creatures, small creatures.
fast creatures, slow creatures, short creatures, tall creatures
God created all the earth,
I know, I know, I know.

For other verses the names of animals may replace
'earth'.
e.g. 'God created all the tigers' . . .
then, 'there were fat tigers, thin tigers', etc.

35 God gave me hands

Steve Kersys

Phil Burt

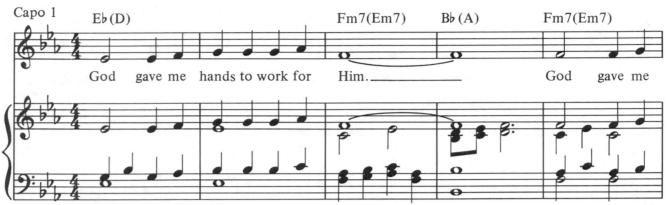

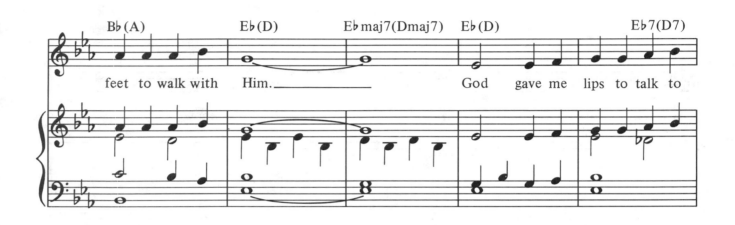

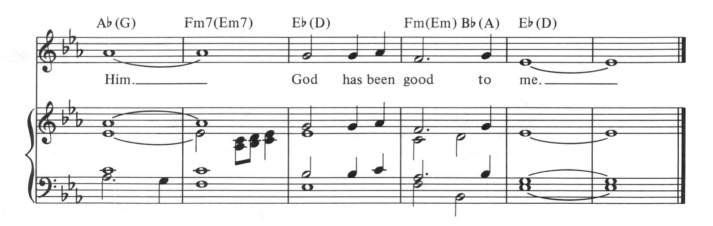

1 God gave me hands to work for Him.
God gave me feet to walk with Him.
God gave me lips to talk to Him.
God has been good to me.

2 God gave me hands to help my friends.
God gave me feet to walk with my friends.
God gave me lips to talk to my friends.
I must be good to my friends.

36 God hears me

Johanna Puls

Ellen R. Thompson

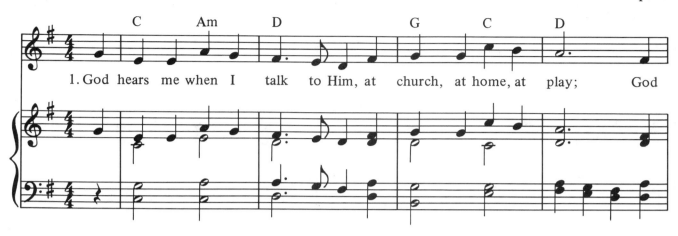

1. God hears me when I talk to Him, at church, at home, at play; God

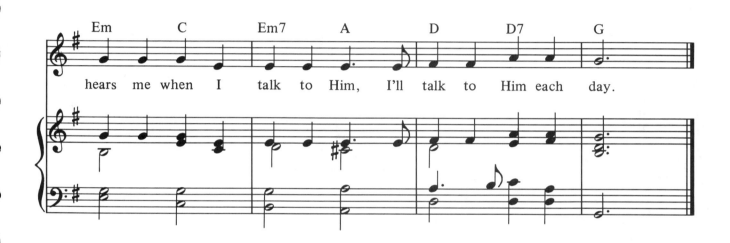

hears me when I talk to Him, I'll talk to Him each day.

1 God hears me when I talk to Him,
  at church, at home, at play;
  God hears me when I talk to Him,
  I'll talk to Him each day.

2 God hears me when I talk to Him,
  I tell Him of my fun;
  I thank Him for my happy times,
  the pleasant things I've done.

3 God hears me when I talk to Him,
  I pray for others too;
  if they are sick or sad or glad,
  He knows just what to do.

37 God has given me His word

R.F. Silver
Capo 3
In a steady two.

Andy Silver

(vl.) God has gi - ven me His word for in - struc - tion, for it shows me how to live day by day. It will guide and it will give me cor - rec - tion,

tel - ling me what God has to say, _____

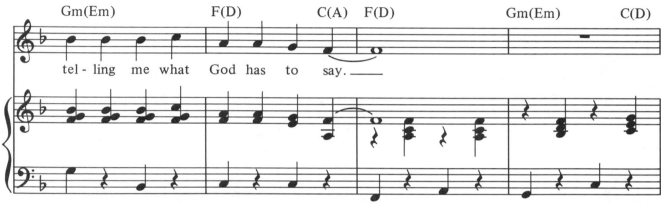

tel - ling me what God has to say. ____

after last verse only.

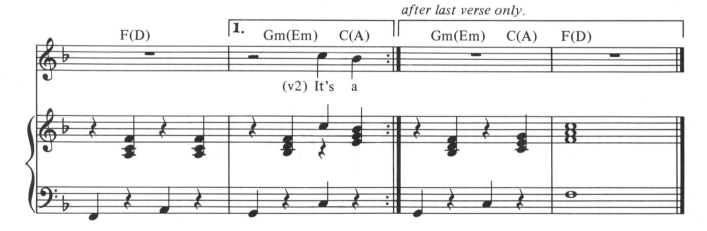

(v2) It's a

1 God has given me His word for instruction,
for it shows me how to live day by day.
It will guide and it will give me correction,
telling me what God has to say,
telling me what God has to say.

2 It's a light to help me see where I'm going,
it's a map to help me walk the right way,
and it points me in God's chosen direction,
telling me what God has to say
telling me what God has to say.

3 It's a sword to fight the foe in the battle,
it's a tool that helps me know how to pray,
it will fill my life with truth and with power,
telling me what God has to say
telling me what God has to say.

4 It's a book that gives the truth about Jesus,
it's a record of the price that He paid,
and it makes me see how much Jesus loves me,
telling me what God has to say
telling me what God has to say.

38 God is good we come before Him

E.M. Nevill

A.H. Brown
Arr. Phil Burt

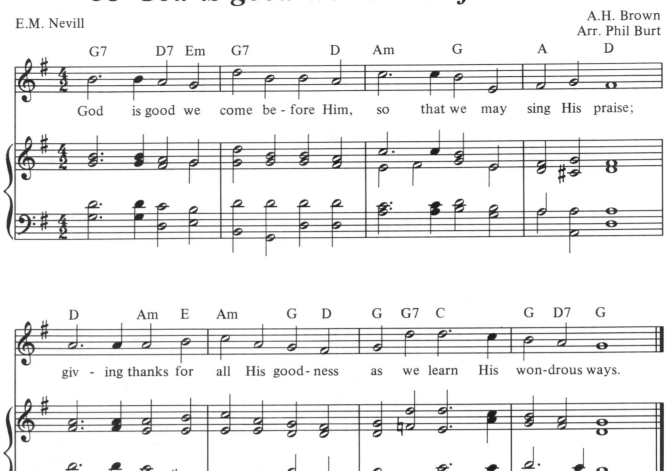

God is good we come be-fore Him, so that we may sing His praise; giv - ing thanks for all His good-ness as we learn His won-drous ways.

1 God is good, we come before Him,
  so that we may sing His praise;
  giving thanks for all His goodness,
  as we learn His wondrous ways.

2 God is great, we come before Him,
  so that we may bow in prayer;
  seeking strength to fight our battles,
  knowing He is everywhere.

3 God is wise, we come before Him
  so that we may know His law;
  learning from the men of old time
  how to serve Him more and more.

39 God is so good

Anon
arr. David Peacock

God is so good, God is so good,

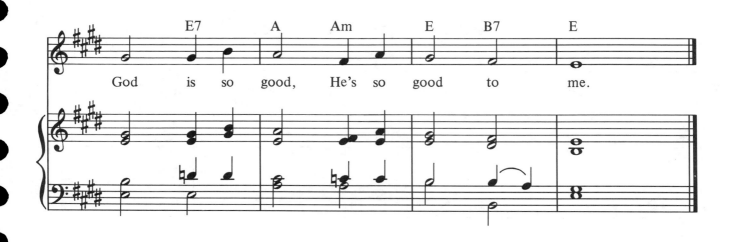

God is so good, He's so good to me.

1 God is so good,
  God is so good,
  God is so good,
  He's so good to me.

2 He took my sin,
  He took my sin,
  He took my sin,
  He's so good to me.

3 Now I am free,
  now I am free,
  now I am free,
  He's so good to me.

4 God is so good,
  He took my sin,
  now I am free,
  He's so good to me.

40 God knows my name

Sandra Maddux

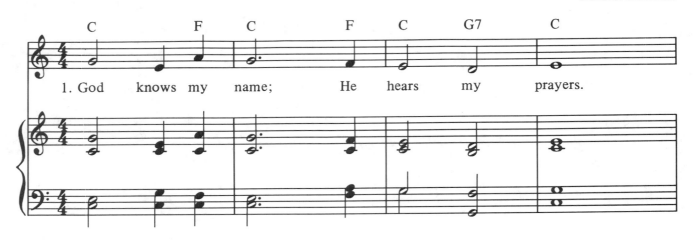

1. God knows my name; He hears my prayers.

When I speak to Him, He al - ways cares.

God knows my name; He hears my prayers.
When I speak to Him, He always cares.

God knows my name; His child I am.
I can talk to Him; that is His plan.

41 God made everything

Doris I. Black

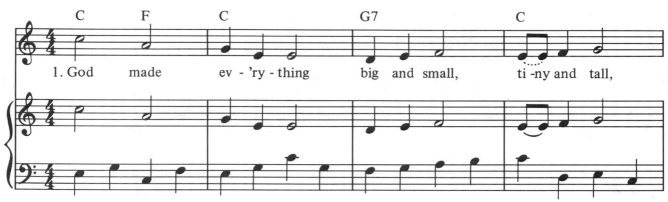

1. God made ev -'ry - thing big and small, ti -ny and tall,

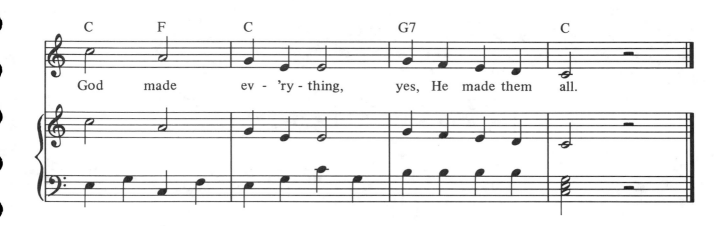

God made ev - 'ry - thing, yes, He made them all.

1 God made everything
  big and small, tiny and tall,
  God made everything,
  yes, He made them all.

2 God made rain to fall,
  rain to fall, rain to fall,
  God made rain to fall,
  yes, He made it fall.

3 God made sun to shine,
  sun to shine, sun to shine,
  God made sun to shine,
  yes, He made it shine.

4 God made birds to sing,
  tweet, tweet, tweet, tweet, tweet, tweet,
  God made birds to sing,
  yes, He made them sing.

42 God made the colours

Peter Lewis

God made the co-lours of the rain-bow yel-low, red and blue,

God made the co-lours of the rain-bow just for me and you.

God made the co-lours of the flo-wers, pur-ple, blue and red

God made the co-lours of the flo-wers in our flo-wer bed.

God made the colours of the rainbow,
yellow, red and blue,
God made the colours of the rainbow,
just for me and you.

1 God made the colours of the flowers,
   purple, blue and red,
   God made the colours of the flowers,
   in our flowerbed.
     God made the colours . . .

2 God made the colours of our pictures,
   orange, green and pink,
   God made the colours of our pictures,
   pencils, paint and ink.
     God made the colours . . .

3 God made the colours of the seasons,
   golden, green and white,
   God made the colours of the seasons,
   changing with the light.
     God made the colours . . .

4 God made the colours of the weather,
   yellow, blue and grey,
   God made the colours of the weather,
   different every day.
     God made the colours . . .

43 God made me

Phil Burt

God made me, God made me, God made me,
in my Bi - ble book I read that God made me.

1 God made me, God made me,
   in my Bible book I read that God made me.

2 God loves me, God loves me,
   in my Bible book I read that God loves me.

3 God helps me, God helps me,
   in my Bible book I read that God helps me.

4 God keeps me, God keeps me,
   in my Bible book I read that God keeps me.

44 God said 'March'

Marie H. Frost

God said, 'March, march, march a-round Jer - i - cho.
Left, right, left, right, round and a-round you shall go.'
One time, two times,
three, four, five and six, and the sev-enth time they marched a-round down came the bricks!

God said, 'March, march, march around Jericho.
Left, right, left, right, round and around you shall go'.
One time, two times, three, four, five and six, and the
seventh time they marched around down came the bricks!

45 God so loved the world

Peter Horrobin
arr. Phil Burt

When group 1 gets to * group 2 starts at beginning

1　God so loved the world He sent to us Jesus,
　　God so loved the world He sent His Son.
　　Alleluia Jesus, Lord Jesus, Jesus;
　　Alleluia Jesus, God sent His Son.

2　Jesus showed the world the love of the Father,
　　Jesus showed the world how we must love.
　　Alleluia Jesus, Lord Jesus, Jesus;
　　Alleluia Jesus, God sent His son.

46 God takes good care of me

E.J. Fischer

1 God takes good care of me each day.
   He keeps me safe at home and play,
   yes, God takes care, good care, of me.
   He takes good care of me.

2 God gives me food and clothes to wear,
   so many things that show His care,
   yes, God takes care, good care, of me.
   He takes good care of me.

3 God sent His Son on Christmas night,
   as stars above were shining bright,
   yes, God takes care, good care, of me.
   He takes good care of me.

47 God told Joshua

Greg Leavers
arr. Phil Burt

God told Jo - shua_ to take Je ri - cho,_

God told Jo - shua_ to take Je ri - cho,_ He said 'Do it my way,'_

Josh - ua said 'O, K,'_ So through faith the ci - ty walls came_ down!_

1. Mar - ching round the ci - ty, _ Priests are at the front,

blow-ing on their trum-pets,— go - ing round just once, this they did for six days,—

just as God had said, the Priests were ma-king all the noise the rest were say-ing!

God told Joshua to take Jericho,
God told Joshua to take Jericho,
He said 'Do it My way,'
Joshua said 'OK'
So through faith the city walls came down!

1 Marching round the city
   Priests are at the front,
   blowing on their trumpets,
   going round just once,
   this they did for six days,
   just as God had said,
   the Priests were making all the noise the rest were saying!
   God told Joshua . . . . .

2 God said on day seven,
   'Here is what you do,
   march around for six times,
   then do something new,
   when you're on lap seven,
   Jericho look out!
   All their walls will crumble when you give a great big SHOUT !!
   God told Joshua . . . . .

48 God's children

Joan Robinson

God's chil-dren, God's chil-dren, we are God's chil-dren, God's chil dren,

God's chil-dren, we are God's chil-dren, and our hea-ven-ly Fa-ther loves us and

we love Him too, and our hea-ven-ly Fa-ther loves us and we love Him too.

God's children, God's children, we are God's children,
God's children, God's children, we are God's children,
and our heavenly Father loves us and we love Him too,
and our heavenly Father loves us and we love Him too.

49 Great is His love

Joan Robinson

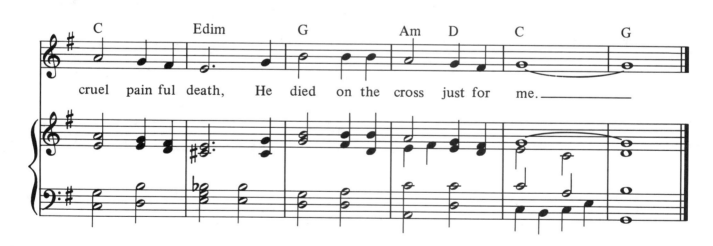

Great is His love, great is His love,
great is His love for me.
He died on the cross, a cruel painful death,
He died on the cross just for me.

50 God cares for you and me

Traditional
arr. Greg Leavers

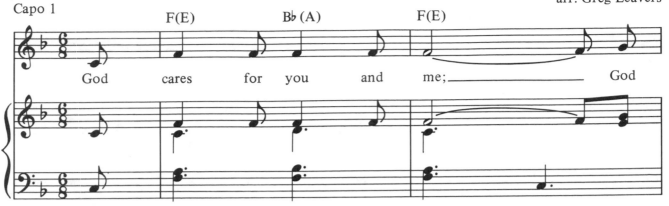

1 God cares for you and me;
  God cares for you and me;
  He gives us home and food and clothes;
  God cares for you and me.

2 God cares for you and me;
  God cares for you and me;
  I learn at Sunday School and church,*
  God cares for you and me.

For this line substitute these words when appropriate:

He lights the sky with stars at night.
He sends His shining angels bright.
He gives us aunts and uncles dear.

If accompanying the song with guitar only. the chords in [ ] need not be played

51 God is near

Marjorie Allen Anderson

Capo 1

In the morn-ing when I rise, when I o-pen up my eyes,

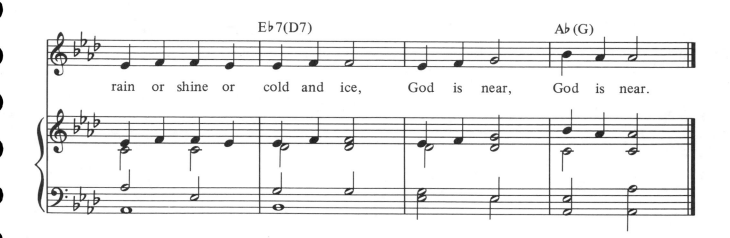

rain or shine or cold and ice, God is near, God is near.

1 In the morning when I rise,
   when I open up my eyes,
   rain or shine or cold and ice,
   God is near, God is near.

2 When I help and when I play,
   He is there to show the way,
   close beside me all the day,
   God is near, God is near.

3 Then when I turn off the light,
   when I go to sleep at night,
   I am always in His sight,
   God is near, God is near.

52 God made the rain to fall

Traditional
arr. Greg Leavers

Capo 1

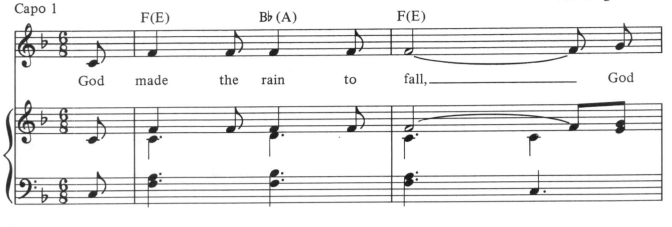

God made the rain to fall,_____ God

made the rain to fall. All things were

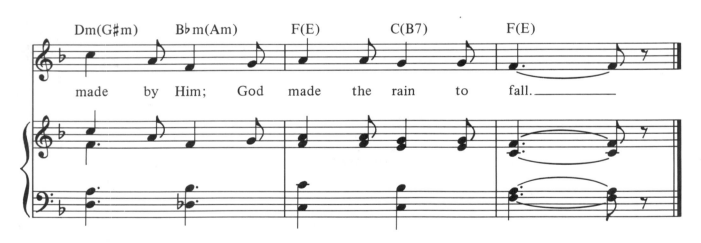

made by Him; God made the rain to fall._____

God made the rain to fall,
God made the rain to fall.
All things were made by Him;
God made the rain to fall.

(sun to shine, flowers grow
stars to shine, etc . . .)

53 Hallelu, hallelu

Composer unknown
arr. Phil Burt

Hal-le-lu, hal-le-lu, hal-le-lu, hal-le-lu -jah; we'll praise the Lord! Hal-le-lu, hal-le-lu, hal-le-lu, hal-le-lu -jah; we'll praise the Lord! We'll praise the Lord, hal-le-lu - jah! We'll praise the Lord, hal-le-lu - jah! We'll praise the Lord, hal-le-lu - jah! We'll praise the Lord!

Hallelu, hallelu, hallelu, hallelujah;
we'll praise the Lord!
Hallelu, hallelu, hallelu, hallelujah;
we'll praise the Lord!

We'll praise the Lord, hallelujah!
We'll praise the Lord, hallelujah!
We'll praise the Lord, hallelujah!
We'll praise the Lord!

54 Happy the day

Joan Robinson
arr. Phil Burt

1. Happy the day the baby was born,
baby was born, baby was born.
Happy the day the baby was born,
bringing salvation to the world.

2 Jesus was the baby's name,
baby's name, baby's name.
Jesus was the baby's name,
bringing salvation to the world.

3 Jesus was the Son of God,
Son of God, Son of God.
Jesus was the Son of God,
bringing salvation to the world.

4 Happy the day the baby was born,
baby was born, baby was born.
Happy the day the baby was born,
bringing salvation to the world.

55 He cares for me

Anon
arr. Phil Burt

He cares for me, He cares for me, I

know He cares for me. If Je - sus cared for

lit - tle boy,* I know He cares for me.

1 He cares for me,
He cares for me,
I know He cares for me.
If Jesus cared for little boy,*
I know He cares for me.

2 He loves me too,
He loves me too,
I know He loves me too.
If Jesus loved the little boy,*
I know He loves me too.

* See John 4. 46-54

56 Have you seen the pussy cat?

Composer unknown
arr. Andy Silver

Have you seen the pus - sy cat, sit - ting on the wall?

Have you heard his beau - ti - ful purr? *(purr)*

Have you seen the li - on stalk - ing round his prey?

Have you heard his ter - ri - ble roar? *(roar)* *One so big,*

one so small, our heaven-ly Fa - ther cares for them all.

One so big, one so small, our heaven-ly Fa - ther cares.

1   Have you seen the pussy eat, sitting on the wall?
    Have you heard his beautiful purr? *(purr)*
    Have you seen the lion stalking round his prey?
    Have you heard his terrible roar? *(roar)*
        One so big, one so small,
        our heavenly Father cares for them all.
        One so big, one so small,
        our heavenly Father cares.

2   Have you seen the children coming home from school?
    Have you heard them shout hurray? *(hurray)*
    Have you seen the grown-ups coming home from work
    saying 'What a horrible day'? *(what a horrible day)*
        Some so big, some so small,
        our heavenly Father cares for them all.
        Some so big, some so small,
        our heavenly Father cares.

57 Hear what God says

Eileen Russell

Hear what God says to you and everyone,
hear what God says to you in His Word;
'I have loved you with an everlasting love.
I have loved you with an everlasting love'.

58 Heaven and earth

Sarah Towers (Age 11)
and Phil Burt

1 Heaven and earth and light and dark,
  sing the creation story.
  Sun, moon, stars, the Universe,
  God made all of these

2 Beautiful flowers and towering trees,
  sing the creation story.
  Green, green grass and ocean blue,
  God made all of these.

3 Singing birds and buzzing bees,
  sing the creation story.
  Swimming fish and roaring lion,
  God made all of these.

4 Little boys and little girls,
  sing the creation story.
  Father, You made it all for us,
  thankyou, thankyou Lord.

59 He is risen

Alice M. Stephens
arr. Ellen R. Thompson

He is risen as He said,
He is risen from the dead,
He lives! He lives! He lives!
He is risen as He said,
He is risen from the dead,
He lives! He lives! He lives!
Oh, yes, He is risen as He said,
He is risen from the dead
and He lives for evermore!

60 He made the sun

Steve Kersys
Capo 3

Phil Burt

He made the sun in the sky,— He made the birds that fly.— He made the rain and snow— and the flo-wers that grow.. He made the stars that shine bright — in the dark, dark — night. He made the riv-ers and seas— and the lea - fy green trees.—

1 He made the sun in the sky,
   He made the birds that fly.
   He made the rain and snow
   and the flowers that grow.
   He made the stars that shine bright
   in the dark, dark night.
   He made the rivers and seas
   and the leafy green trees.

2 He gave me hands that can hold
   and fingers to feel.
   He gave me feet to walk
   and my mouth to talk.
   He gave me ears to hear
   and my eyes to see.
   He gave me Jesus His Son
   who, in love, died for me.

61 Here we come to Bethlehem

Emma F. Bush
arr. Phil Burt

1 Here we come to Bethlehem,
here we come to Bethlehem,
here we come to Bethlehem,
to see the baby Jesus.

2 Here we see the shepherds kneel,
here we see the shepherds kneel,
here we see the shepherds kneel,
before the baby Jesus.

3 Here the wise men bring their gifts,
here the wise men bring their gifts,
here the wise men bring their gifts,
to give the baby Jesus.

4 We will sing on Christmas day,
we will sing on Christmas day,
we will sing on Christmas day,
praise to the baby Jesus.

62 He's got the whole wide world

arr. Phil Burt

He's got the whole wide world _____ in His hands, He's got the whole wide world _____ in His hands, He's got the whole wide world _____ in His hands, He's got the whole world in His hands. He's got the _____ hands.

1 He's got the whole wide world in His hands,
   He's got the whole wide world in His hands,
   He's got the whole wide world in His hands,
   He's got the whole world in His hands.

2 He's got ev'rybody here, in His hands,
   He's got ev'rybody here, in His hands,
   He's got ev'rybody here, in His hands,
   He's got the whole world in His hands.

3 He's got the tiny little baby, in His hands,
   He's got the tiny littly baby, in His hands,
   He's got the tiny little baby, in His hands,
   He's got the whole world in His hands.

4 He's got you and me brother, in His hands,
   He's got you and me brother, in His hands,
   He's got you and me brother, in His hands,
   He's got the whole world in His hands.

63 Here comes Jesus

Lillian Waldecker

1. Here comes Je-sus on a don-key rid-ing, oh, so slow! Lit-tle chil-dren run be-fore Him, sing-ing as they go. *Ho - san - na, ho-san - na, sing-ing all a - long. Ho - san - na, ho-san - na, Je-sus loves their song.*

1 Here comes Jesus on a donkey
   riding, oh, so slow!
   Little children run before Him,
   singing as they go.
   Hosanna, hosanna, singing all along.
   Hosanna, hosanna, Jesus loves their song.

2 People lay their coats before Him,
   as they ride along,
   waving branches, loudly singing,
   hear their happy song.
   Hosanna, . . .

3 In God's house their voices ringing,
   praises loud and long.
   Tho' men try to stop their singing,
   Jesus wants their song.
   Hosanna, . . .

64 Hey, do you love Jesus?

Capo 1

Refrain: F. Whitfield
Arr. Betty Pulkingham

With simplicity

(Question) Hey, (name) do you love Je - sus? (Answer) Yes, I love Je - sus. (Q)Are you sure you love Je - sus? (A)Yes I'm sure I love Je - sus.(Q)Tell me, why do you love Je - sus? (A)This is why I love Je - sus,(All)be - cause He first loved me. Yes I love Him, this is why___ I love Him.

The first part of this song is a dialogue.
One person starts it and the one who is named sings the answers,
and in turn asks the questions the second time round.
A good concluding verse is 'Hey saints' (or 'family' or 'kids') . . .
some term which includes all of those present.

Hey (name) do you love Jesus?
(answer) Yes, I love Jesus.
Are you sure you love Jesus?
(answer) Yes I'm sure I love Jesus.
Tell me, why do you love Jesus?
(answer) This is why I love Jesus,
(All) because He first loved me.
Yes I love Him, this is why I love Him.

Oh, how I love Jesus,
oh, how I love Jesus,
oh, how I love Jesus,
because He first loved me.
Yes, I love Him, this is why I love Him.

65 Hooray for Jesus

Anon
arr. Phil Burt

Hoo - ray — for Je - sus, hoo - ray — for Je - sus,

some one in the crowd is shou ting hoo-ray for Je - sus. One two three four

who are we shou ting for? Je - sus that's who.

Hoo - ray — for Je - sus, hoo - ray — for Je - sus,

Hooray for Jesus, hooray for Jesus
someone in the crowd is shouting hooray for Jesus.
One two three four who are we shouting for?
Jesus that's who.
Hooray for Jesus, hooray for Jesus,
someone in the crowd is shouting hooray for Jesus.
Five six seven eight, who do we appreciate?
Jesus that's who.

66 How did Moses cross the Red Sea?

arr. Phil Burt

Lyrics:

How did Mo-ses cross the Red Sea? How did Mo-ses cross the Red Sea? How did Mo-ses cross the Red Sea? How did he get a-cross? Did he swim? No! No! Did he row? No! No! Did he jump? No! No! No! No! Did he drive? No! No! Did he fly? No! No! How

How did Moses cross the Red Sea?
How did Moses cross the Red Sea?
How did Moses cross the Red Sea?
How did he get across?
Did he swim? No! No!
Did he row? No! No!
Did he jump? No! No! No! No!
Did he drive? No! No!
Did he fly? No! No!
How did he get across?
God blew with His wind, puff, puff, puff, puff.
He blew just enough, 'nough, 'nough, 'nough, 'nough,
and through the sea He made a path,
that's how he got across.

67 How many fingers?

Dot Cachiaras
Arr. Michelle Pittinger

Capo 3

1 Hold up fingers.   2 Snap fingers.   3 Nod head.

1   How many fingers? *(Hold up fingers)*
Snap, snappy fingers? *(Snap fingers)*
I'm pretty sure I know! *(Nod head)*
Ten snappy fingers, *(Hold up fingers)*
snap, snappy fingers, *(Snap fingers)*
I'm pretty sure I know. *(Nod head)*

2   How many shoulders? *(Hands on shoulders.)*
Tap-tappy shoulders? *(Tap shoulders.)*
I'm pretty sure I know! *(Nod head.)*
Two tappy shoulders, *(Hold up two fingers.)*
tap-tappy shoulders, *(Tap shoulders.)*
I'm pretty sure I know! *(Nod head.)*

3 How many toeses? *(Point to toes.)*
   Tip-tippy toeses? *(Walk on tiptoes.)*
   I'm pretty sure I know! *(Nod head.)*
   Ten-tippy toeses, *(Hold up ten fingers.)*
   tip-tippy toeses, *(Walk on tiptoes.)*
   I'm pretty sure I know! *(Nod head.)*

4 How many noses? *(Point to nose.)*
   Wig-wiggly noses? *(Wiggle nose.)*
   I'm pretty sure I know! *(Nod head.)*
   One wiggly nose, *(Hold up one finger.)*
   wig-wiggly nose, *(Wiggle nose.)*
   I'm pretty sure I know! *(Nod head.)*

5 How many kneeses? *(Touch knees.)*
   Bend-bendy kneeses? *(Bend knees.)*
   I'm pretty sure I know! *(Nod head.)*
   Two bendy kneeses, *(Hold up two fingers.)*
   bend-bendy kneeses, *(Bend knees.)*
   I'm pretty sure I know! *(Nod head.)*

6 How many clappers? *(Hold up hands.)*
   Clap-clappy clappers? *(Clap hands.)*
   I'm pretty sure I know! *(Nod head.)*
   Two clappy clappers, *(Hold up two fingers.)*
   clap-clappy clappers, *(Clap hands.)*
   I'm pretty sure I know! *(Nod head.)*

7 How many elbows? *(Stick out elbows.)*
   Craze, crazy elbows? *(Touch elbows.)*
   I'm pretty sure I know! *(Nod head.)*
   Two crazy elbows, *(Hold up two fingers.)*
   craze, crazy elbows, *(Touch elbows.)*
   I'm pretty sure I know! *(Nod head.)*

8 Thank You, dear Father, *(Fold hands to pray)*
   dear heav'nly Father,
   ten fingers, toes, one nose, *(Wiggle fingers,
     rise up on toes, point to nose.)*
   two hands that clap-clap, *(Clap hands.)*
   shoulders to tap-tap, *(Tap shoulders.)*
   two knees and two elbows. *(Bend knees,
     touch elbows.)*

68 How do I know?

D. Parsons

How do I know that God loves me? He tells me so and I trust Him. How do I know He forgives me? He tells me so and it's true. He tells me so in the Bible, He tells me so and it's true.

How do I know that God loves me?
He tells me so and I trust Him.
How do I know He forgives me?
He tells me so and it's true.
He tells me so in the Bible,
He tells me so and it's true.

69 I have the joy

George W. Cooke
arr. Phil Burt

I have the joy, joy, joy, joy, down in ___ my heart, (where?)

down in ___ my heart, (where?) down in ___ my heart, I have the joy, joy, joy, joy,

down in ___ my heart, (where?) down in ___ my heart to stay. ___

1 I have the joy, joy, joy, joy,
   down in my heart, (where?)
   down in my heart, (where?)
   down in my heart.
   I have the joy, joy, joy, joy,
   down in my heart, (where?)
   down in my heart to stay.

2 I have the peace that passes understanding
   down in my heart, (where?)
   down in my heart, (where?)
   down in my heart.

I have the peace that passes understanding
down in my heart, (where?)
down in my heart to stay.

3 I have the love of Jesus, love of Jesus
   down in my heart, (where?)
   down in my heart, (where?)
   down in my heart.
   I have the love of Jesus, love of Jesus,
   down in my heart, (where?)
   down in my heart to stay.

70 *I am the Way*

Capo 1

arr. Phil Burt

Can be sung as a 3-part round

I am the Way, the Truth, and the Life,
I am the Way, the Truth, and the Life.
No one comes to the Father but by Me.

71 I can talk to God

Gertrude Shannon
arr. Phil Burt

I can talk to God.
I can talk to God.
I know that He is listening,
I can talk to God.

72 If I had a boat

Greg Leavers
arr. Phil Burt

If I had a boat (If I had a boat) on Ga-li-lee ___ (on Ga-li-lee). ___ Just an or-di-na-ry boat (Just an or-di-na-ry boat) on Ga-li-lee ___ (on Ga-li-lee). ___ Then if Je-sus should walk down the shore, I'd in-vite Him in so He could

tell me more a-bout— fol-low-ing Him (a-bout fol-low-ing Him), right

in (You'd better believe it!) my job.——

1 If I had a boat (If I had a boat)
   on Galilee (on Galilee).
   Just an ordinary boat (Just an ordinary boat)
   on Galilee (on Galilee).
   Then if Jesus had walked down the shore,
   I'd invite Him in so He could tell me more
   about following Him (about following Him),
   right in (you'd better believe it) my job.

2 If I had a house (If I had a house)
   in Jericho (in Jericho).
   Just an ordinary house (Just an ordinary house)
   in Jericho (in Jericho).
   Then I'd let the sick folk all come in,
   so that Jesus could make them well again
   and they would listen to Him (and they would listen to Him),
   right in (you'd better believe it) my home.

3 If I had a house (If I had a house)
   in your street (in your street).
   Just an ordinary house (Just an ordinary house)
   in your street (in your street).
   Then I'd want to talk of Jesus my friend,
   how He gives new life that will never end
   and I'd live for Him (and I'd live for Him),
   right in (you'd better believe it) your street.

73 If I were a butterfly

Brian Howard

If I were a but-ter - fly, I'd thank You Lord for giv - ing me wings. And if I were a ro-bin in a tree, I'd thank You Lord that I could sing. And if I were a fish in the sea,— I'd wig-gle my tail and I'd gig -gle with glee, but

1 If I were a butterfly,
   I'd thank You Lord for giving me wings.
   And if I were a robin in a tree,
   I'd thank You Lord that I could sing.
   And if I were a fish in the sea,
   I'd wiggle my tail and I'd giggle with glee,
   but I just thank You Father for making me 'me'.

   For You gave me a heart
   and You gave me a smile.
   You gave me Jesus and
   You made me Your child.
   And I just thank You Father for making me 'me'.

2 If I were an elephant,
   I'd thank You Lord by raising my trunk.
   And if I were a kangaroo,
   You know I'd hop right up to You.
   And if I were an octopus,
   I'd thank You Lord for my fine looks,
   but I just thank You Father for making me 'me'.
     For You gave me . . .

3 If I were a wiggly worm,
   I'd thank You Lord that I could squirm.
   And if I were a billy goat,
   I'd thank You Lord for my strong throat.
   And if I were a fuzzy wuzzy bear,
   I'd thank You Lord for my fuzzy wuzzy hair,
   but I just thank You Father for making me 'me'.
     For You gave me . . .

74 I can talk to God, He will hear

J. Sibley

E.H. Swinstead

1 I can talk to God,
He will hear my prayers.
I can talk to God
for I know He cares.
He will listen when I say,
'Thank You for Your love today,
for Your help in every way,
Oh, Thank You, God'.

2 I can talk to God,
He will hear my prayers.
I can talk to God
for I know He cares.

He will listen when I say,
'I have done wrong things today,
Please forgive me now I pray,
forgive me, God'.

3 I can talk to God,
He will hear my prayers.
I can talk to God
for I know He cares.
He will listen when I say,
'please help all my friends today,
help them in their work and play,
please help them, God'.

75 If the Lord be God

Sarah Eberle

If the Lord be God, follow Him.
If the Lord be God, follow Him.
Elijah on the mountain showed the Lord is God.
If the Lord be God, follow Him.

76 If we confess our sins

Ellis Anne Barr
arr. Phil Burt

Capo 3

If we con-fess our sins, if we con-fess our sins, He is faith-ful and just to for - give us our sins and to cleanse us from all___ un - right-eous-ness, if we con-fess our sins,___ if we con-fess our sins.

If we confess our sins, if we confess our sins,
He is faithful and just to forgive us our sins
and to cleanse us from all unrighteousness,
if we confess our sins, if we confess our sins.

77 *I have a message for you*

Mary A. Barbour
arr. Phil Burt

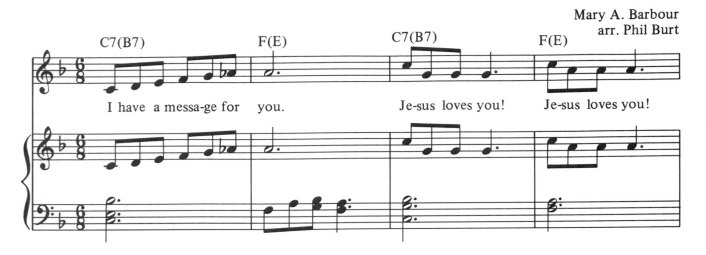

I have a messa-ge for you. Je-sus loves you! Je-sus loves you!

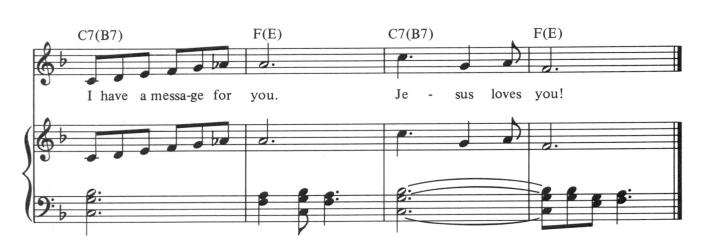

I have a messa-ge for you. Je - sus loves you!

I have a message for you.
Jesus loves you!
Jesus loves you!
I have a message for you.
Jesus loves you!

78 I love the sun

Gwen F. Smith

1 I love the sun, it shines on __ me,

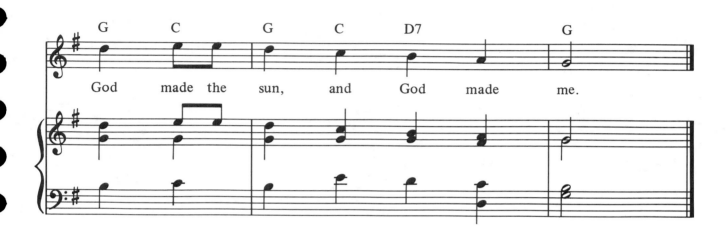

God made the sun, and God made me.

1 I love the sun,
   it shines on me,
   God made the sun,
   and God made me.

2 I love the stars,
   they twinkle on me,
   God made the stars,
   and God made me.

3 I love the rain,
   it splashes on me,
   God made the rain,
   and God made me.

4 I love the wind,
   it blows round me,
   God made the wind,
   and God made me.

5 I love the birds,
   they sing to me,
   God made the birds,
   and God made me.

79 I know that I'm only a child

S. & J. Doddridge
arr. Phil Burt

know-ing ev'-ry move I___ make,___   rea - dy___   al-ways to guide.

___ me___ Lord   ev - en when I make a mis - take._____

I know that I'm only a child O Lord
but I know that You listen to me.
I know that I'm only a child O Lord,
but You'll always listen to me.

1 You're always there beside me
   knowing every move I make,
   ready always to guide me Lord
   even when I make a mistake.
      I know that I'm . . .

2 No matter what the problem
   nothing's to big for You,
   You will never ignore me Lord;
   You've always got time, it's true.
      I know that I'm . . .

3 I don't even have to shout out Lord
   for You to hear my prayers,
   and You will always answer me,
   I know that You'll always be there.
      I know that I'm . . .

80 I look out through the doorway

Greg Leavers
arr. Phil Burt

I look out through the door - way,_ who's that I see be-fore me?_ My young son com - ing_ home._ I must run to meet him,_ hug him when I greet him,_ and say 'Son, wel - come_ home'. We will have a - par ty_ and

I look out through the doorway,
who's that I see before me?
My young son coming home.
I must run to meet him,
hug him when I greet him,
and say 'Son, welcome home.
We will have a party
and I can't wait to start,
he must have the very finest food,
the best robe, ring and sandals.
He was lost, but now is found,
welcome home, son, welcome home.

81 I may never march in the infantry

arr. Andy Silver

I may ne - ver

march in the in - fan-try, ride with the cav - al-ry, shoot with the ar-til - le-ry,

I may ne - ver zoom o'er the e - ne-my, for I'm in the Lord's ar -

my. I'm in the Lord's ar - my (Yes Sir!), I'm in the Lord's ar -

I may never march in the infantry,
ride with the cavalry, shoot with the artillery,
I may never zoom o'er the enemy,
for I'm in the Lord's army.
I'm in the Lord's army (Yes Sir!),
I'm in the Lord's army (Yes Sir!).
I may never march in the infantry,
ride with the cavalry, shoot with the artillery,
I may never zoom o'er the enemy,
for I'm in the Lord's army.

82 I spy with my little eye

Greg Leavers
arr. Phil Burt

I spy with my lit - tle eye,

some thing be - gin - ing with 'L'.

Is it a li - on or is it a light?

No it's my leg, not my left but my right.

1 I spy with my little eye
   something beginning with 'L'.
   Is it a lion or is it a light?
   No, it's my leg, not my left but my right.

2 I spy with my little eye
   something beginning with 'O'.
   Is it an onion or is it an owl?
   No, it's an orange to eat for my tea.

3 I spy with my little eye
   something beginning with 'V'.
   Is it a violin or is it a vole?
   No, it's a van driven by the postman.

4 I spy with my little eye
   something beginning with 'E'.
   Is it an elephant, is it an eye?
   No, it's your ear which helps you to hear.

4 L, O, V, and an E;
   What word do those letters spell?
   Something that Jesus has shown to us all;
   now you all know, the letters spell 'LOVE'.

83 I want to tell you

In the verse the leader sings a phrase and
then everybody else repeats it.

Greg Leavers
arr. Phil Burt

I want_ to tell you (I want_ to tell you) my eyes are blue

(my eyes are blue), I want_ to show you (I want_ to show you)

what I can do [clap! clap!] (what I can do [clap! clap!]), *There's no-one, NOT ONE, in the*

world like me,___ I'm so ve - ry, ve - ry, ve - ry, ve - ry

spe - cial you see.___ There's no - one, NOT ONE,___ in the

world like me,___ for God made me just the way He wan - ted me to be.___

1 I want to tell you (I want to tell you)
my eyes are blue (my eyes are blue),
I want to show you (I want to show you)
what I can do (clap! clap!) (what I can do) (clap! clap!).

There's no-one, NOT ONE, in the world like me,
I'm so very, very, very, very special you see.
There's no-one, NOT ONE, in the world like me,
for God made me just the way He wanted me to be.

2 There are so many (there are so many)
things I can do (things I can do).
I don't feel useless (I don't feel useless)
these words are true (these words are true).
   There's no-one . . .

3 Jesus is special (Jesus is special),
I'm special too (I'm special too).
He says He loves me (He says He loves me)
and He loves you (and He loves you).
   There's no-one . . .

84 I'm a footstep follower

Greg Leavers
arr. Phil Burt

I'm a foot-step___ fol-low-er___ for Je-sus leads___ the way. He knows the life___ that's___ best for me:___ a plan for ev'-ry___ day, as I walk and talk with Him.___ He'll___ ne-ver let me

I'm a footstep follower
for Jesus leads the way.
He knows the life that's best for me:
a plan for every day,
as I walk and talk with Him.
He'll never let me stray.
I'm a foostep follower
for Jesus leads the way.

85 I'm all made of hinges

arr. Phil Burt

1 I'm all made of hinges and everything bends,
   from the top of my head way down to my ends.
   I'm hinges in front and I'm hinges in back,
   if I didn't have hinges I surely would crack.

2 I'm glad that God made me so I can do things,
   like playing with toys and sitting on swings.
   It's fun to bend over and sit on the floor,
   and hinges allow me to do this and more.

86 I'm giving

Mary Le. Barr
Capo 1:E

A. Vivienne Blomguist
arr. Phil Burt

I'm giv - ing, I'm giv - ing be - cause I love

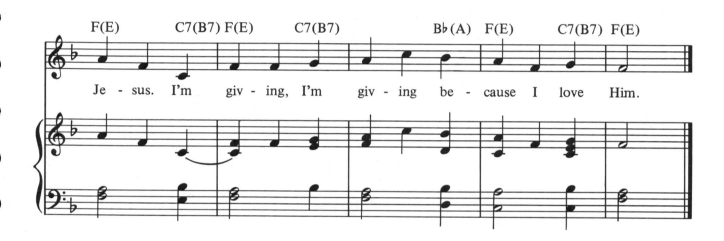

Je - sus. I'm giv - ing, I'm giv - ing be - cause I love Him.

1 I'm giving, I'm giving
   because I love Jesus.
   I'm giving, I'm giving
   because I love Him.

2 I'm singing, I'm singing
   because I love Jesus.
   I'm singing, I'm singing
   because I love Him.

3 I'm helping, I'm helping
   because I love Jesus.
   I'm helping, I'm helping
   because I love Him.

87 I'm going to take a step of faith

Greg Leavers
arr. Phil Burt

Capo 3

I'm going to take (clap! clap!) a step of___ faith,___ I'm going to
put my trust in the Lord.___
He has___ the po-wer___ to car-ry me through,___ if I
lis - ten care - ful - ly, He'll tell me what to do. I'm going to

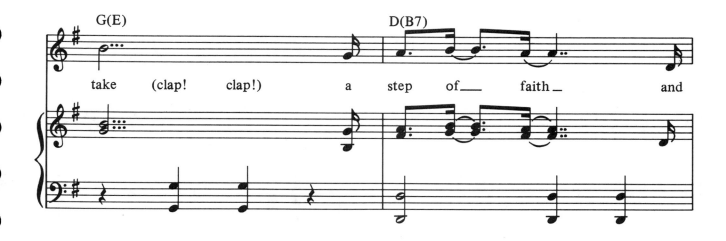

take (clap! clap!) a step of__ faith _ and

put my__ trust_ in the Lord. _

1 I'm going to take a step of faith,
   I'm going to put my trust in the Lord.
   He has the power to carry me through,
   if I listen carefully, He'll tell me what to do.
   I'm going to take a step of faith
   and put my trust in the Lord.

2 I'm going to take a step of faith,
   I'm going to put my trust in the Lord.
   He made a promise He loves me so,
   wherever He might lead me, He'll never let me go.
   I'm going to take a step of faith
   and put my trust in the Lord.

88 In and out the stars

Joan Robinson
arr. Phil Burt

1 In and out the stars of the Universe,
   in and out the stars of the Universe,
   in and out the stars of the Universe,
   seeing what a great creator our God is.

2 In and out the flowers and the trees of the earth . . .

3 In and out the animals that roam the earth . . .

4 In and out my friends and my Mum and Dad . . .

89 I'm so glad

Ethel M. Greenawalt

arr. Phil Burt

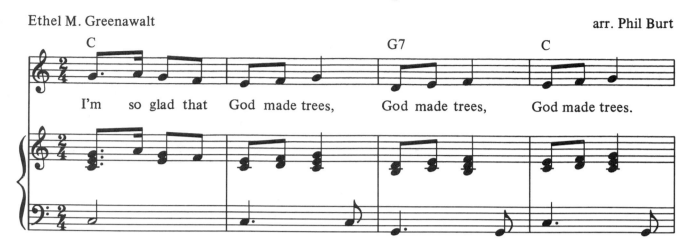

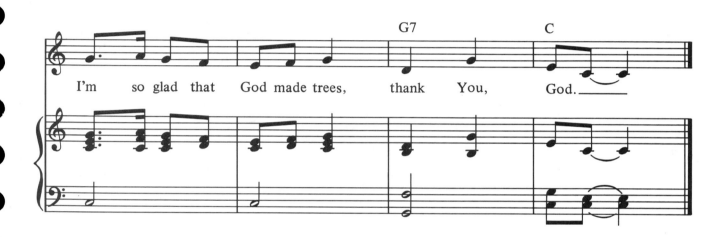

1 I'm so glad that God made trees,
God made trees, God made trees.
I'm so glad that God made trees,
thank You, God.

2 I'm so glad that God made flowers.

3 I'm so glad that God made sky.

4 I'm so glad that God made birds.

5 I'm so glad that God made rain.

6 I'm so glad that God made me.

90 In everything that I do

Ian White

In ev'ry-thing that I do show me what Je-sus would do. In ev'ry-thing that I do show me what Je-sus would do. I will not be a-fraid for

I can al - ways pray. Show me what

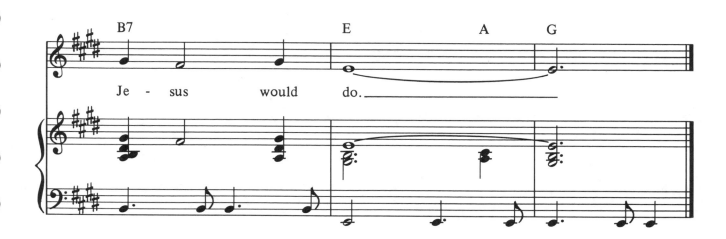

Je - sus would do._____

In everything that I do
show me what Jesus would do.
In everything that I do
show me what Jesus would do.
I will not be afraid
for I can always pray.
Show me what Jesus would do.

91 In our work and in our play

W.G. Wills

B. Milgrove

In our work and in our play, Jesus, ever with us stay.

May we serve You all our days, true and faithful in our ways.

1 In our work and in our play.
   Jesus, ever with us stay.
   May we serve You all our days,
   true and faithful in our ways.

2 May we in Your strength subdue
   evil tempers, words untrue,
   thoughts impure and deeds unkind,
   all things hateful to Your mind.

3 Jesus, from Your throne above,
   fill anew our hearts with love.
   So that what we say and do
   shows that we belong to You.

4 Children of the King are we,
   may we loyal to Him be.
   Try to please Him every day,
   in our work and in our play.

92 In the morning

M.A. Anderson

Phil Burt

1 In the morning when I rise,
   when I open up my eyes,
   rain or shine or cold and ice,
   God is near.

2 When I help and when I play,
   He is there to show the way,
   close beside me all the day,
   God is near.

3 Then when I turn off the light,
   when I go to sleep at night,
   I am always in His sight,
   God is near.

93 In the beginning

J.R. Willanger
arr. Phil Burt

Capo 3

In the be - gin - ning the Lord God
said, on the first day of the
world, 'Let there be dark and light', and there
was day and night, and the Lord saw it was good!

1 In the beginning the Lord God said,
  on the first day of the world,
  'Let there be dark and light',
  and there was day and night,
  and the Lord saw it was good!

2 In the beginning the Lord God said,
  on the second day of the world,
  'Let there be waters here,
  and the heavens be there',
  and the Lord saw it was good!

3 In the beginning the Lord God said,
  on the third day of the world,
  'Let there be earth and seas,
  let there be flowers and trees',
  and the Lord saw it was good!

4 In the beginning the Lord God said,
  on the fourth day of the world,
  'Let there be sun for light,
  moon and stars for the night',
  and the Lord saw it was good!

5 In the beginning the Lord God said,
  on the fifth day of the world,
  'Let the birds fly and sing,
  and the fish dive and swim',
  and the Lord saw it was good!

6 In the beginning the Lord God said,
  on the sixth day of the world,
  'Let the animals be on land,
  let us make man and woman',
  and the Lord saw it was good!

7 In the beginning the Lord God said,
  on the seventh day of the world,
  'For My use all is blessed,
  and I now take a rest,
  for My world is very good!'

94 It is a good thing

Sarah Eberle

It is a good thing
to give thanks to the Lord;
it is a good thing, a good thing.
It is a good thing
to give thanks to the Lord;
it is a good, good thing.

95 I want to work for Jesus

J. Fischer
Capo 3

E. Thompson

I want to work for Jesus, I want to help and share,
for He needs happy helpers, to serve Him everywhere.
At home, at school, at play-time, I'll try to do what's fair,
and be a friend to others by doing my part there.

96 It was Jesus

Andy Silver

Capo 3

It was Je-sus who taught His dis - ci - ples. It was

Je - sus who called them by name. Then one night on the lake came the

wind and the rain and the waves splashed right ov - er the boat.

(Chorus)

Splish, splash, pit - ter pit - ter pat, down came the storm with a

bang and a crash,_ splish, splash, pit - ter pit - ter pat,

down came the storm with a bang and a crash._

1 It was Jesus who taught His disciples,
   it was Jesus who called them by name.
   Then one night on the lake came the wind and the rain,
   and the waves splashed right over the boat.

   Splish, splash, pitter pitter pat,
   down came the storm with a bang and a crash,
   splish, splash, pitter pitter pat,
   down came the storm with a bang and a crash.

2 It was Jesus asleep in the trawler,
   it was Jesus who woke to their cries.
   'Don't you care that we drown, we're afraid we'll go down'
   and the waves splashed right over the boat.
   Splish, splash . . .

3 It was Jesus who stood to attention,
   it was Jesus who spoke to the waves.
   'You be quiet, do no harm.' Right away there was calm.
   'Who's this man?' asked the men in the boat.
     Splish, splash . . .

97 I will make you fishers

Harry D. Clarke

fish - ers___ of men, if you fol - low Me.

I will make you fishers of men,
fishers of men, fishers of men;
I will make you fishers of men,
if you follow Me.
If you follow Me, if you follow Me,
I will make you fishers of men,
if you follow Me.

98 I will sing, I will sing

Max Dyer

I will sing, I will sing a song unto the Lord. I will sing, I will sing a song unto the Lord. I will sing, I will sing a song. unto the Lord. Al-le-lu-ia, glo-ry to the Lord. Al-le-lu, al-le-lu-ia, glo-ry to the Lord. Al-le-lu, al-le-lu-ia, glo-ry to the Lord. Al-le-

lu, al-le-lu - ia, glo - ry to the Lord. Al-le - lu - ia, glo - ry to the Lord.

1 I will sing, I will sing a song unto the Lord.
I will sing, I will sing a song unto the Lord.
I will sing, I will sing a song unto the Lord.
Alleluia, glory to the Lord.

   Allelu, alleluia, glory to the Lord.
   Allelu, alleluia, glory to the Lord.
   Allelu, alleluia, glory to the Lord.
   Alleluia, glory to the Lord.

2 We will come, we will come as one before the Lord.
We will come, we will come as one before the Lord.
We will come, we will come as one before the Lord.
Alleluia, glory to the Lord.
   Allelu, alleluia . . .

3 If the Son, if the Son shall make you free,
if the Son, if the Son shall make you free,
if the Son, if the Son shall make you free,
you shall be free indeed.
   Allelu, alleluia . . .

4 In His name, in His name we have the victory.
In His name, in His name we have the victory.
In His name, in His name we have the victory.
Alleluia, glory to the Lord.
   Allelu, alleluia . . .

Most cffective sung unaccompanied,
but with light clapping.
Suggested rhythm:
♩ ♫ ♩ ♫ ♩ etc.

99 It's time to turn

Joan Robinson
arr. Phil Burt

It's time to turn, — it's time to turn, —

it's time to turn — to the Lord.

Lord. Reach and re - ceive all that God has to

give, it's time to turn, time to turn to the

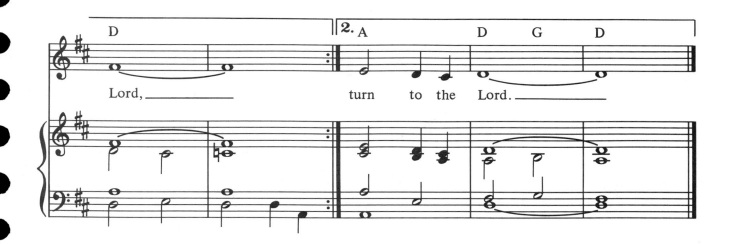

It's time to turn, it's time to turn,
it's time to turn to the Lord.
It's time to turn, it's time to turn,
it's time to turn to the Lord.
Reach and receive all that God has to give
it's time to turn, time to turn to the Lord.
Reach and receive all that God has to give
it's time to turn, time to turn to the Lord.

100 It's a song of praise

Greg Leavers

It's a song of praise, it's a song of
thank - ful - ness, it's a song of joy,
for ev - ery gi - rl and boy,

God gave me my hands,

It's a song of praise,
it's a song of thankfulness,
it's a song of joy
for every girl and boy.

1 God gave me my hands,
    God gave me my voice,
    God gave me a thankful heart
    so now I can rejoice.
        It's a song of praise . . .

2 God gave me my feet,
    God gave me my arms,
    the life and love He gives to me
    makes me want to dance.
        It's a song of praise . . .

101 I will trust

Isaiah 12:2

Stella B. Daleburn

I will trust, I will trust;
I will trust and not be afraid,
I will trust, I will trust
and not be afraid.

102 Jesus bids us shine

Susan Warner

E.O. Excell
(altered)

1 Jesus bids us shine
with a pure, clear light,
like a little candle
burning in the night.
In this world is darkness;
so let us shine,
you in your small corner,
and I in mine.

2 Jesus bids us shine,
first of all for Him;
well He sees and knows it,
if our light grows dim.
He looks down from heaven
to see us shine,
you in your small corner,
and I in mine.

3 Jesus bids us shine,
then, for all around;
many kinds of darkness
in the world are found—
sin, and want and sorrow—
so we must shine,
you in your small corner,
and I in mine.

103 Jesus' friends were looking up

Lillian Waldecker
arr. Phil Burt

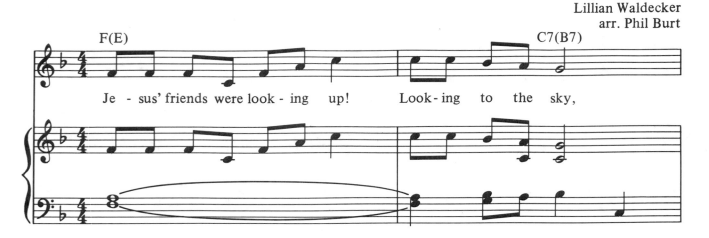

Je - sus' friends were look - ing up! Look - ing to the sky,

they saw Je - sus go - ing up to His home on high.

Actions:

1 Shade eyes with hand, looking up.
2 Raise hands (palms up) little by little.
3 Lower hands (palms down) little by little.

1 Jesus' friends were looking up! ①
Looking to the sky,
they saw Jesus going up ②
to His home on high.

2 Jesus said, 'I'm coming back, ③
I will tell you why.
I will take you up, up, up ②
to My home on high'.

104 Jesus' hands were kind hands

Hopkinson (adapted)

French melody
arr. Phil Burt

Jesus' hands were kind hands doing good to all,
healing pain and sickness, blessing children small,
and my hands should serve Him, ready at His call.
Jesus' hands were kind hands doing good to all.

105 Jesus has promised

Scott Lawrence
arr. Phil Burt

Je - sus has promi - sed my Shep - herd to be,

that's why I love Him so; and to the child - ren He

said 'Come to Me,' that's why I love Him so.

That's why I love Him, that's why I love Him, be-cause He first loved

me. _____ When I'm temp - ted and tried, He is

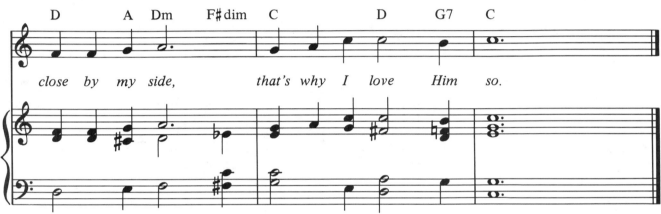

close by my side, that's why I love Him so.

Jesus has promised my Shepherd to be,
that's why I love Him so;
and to the children He said 'Come to Me,'
that's why I love Him so.

*That's why I love Him, that's why I love Him,
because He first loved me.
When I'm tempted and tried, He is close by my side,
that's why I love Him so.*

106 Jesus in the temple

Based on
Luke 2:46-49

John Leinbaugh

Je - sus in the tem - ple, serv - ing God,
sit -ting with the men of the law; ask-ing them some ques - tions and
giv - ing them some an - swers, Je - sus in the tem - ple just a -
mazed them all! Ma - ry and Jo - seph looked for Him.

Jesus in the temple, serving God,
sitting with the men of the law;
asking them some questions and giving them some answers,
Jesus in the temple just amazed them all!
Mary and Joseph looked for Him.
When they found Him, He declared,
'I must be about my Father's work.
I am His and He is mine.'

107 Jesus is a friend of mine

Paul Mazak
arr. Judith Barnard

1 Jesus is a friend of mine
Praise Him!
Jesus is a friend of mine
Praise Him!
Praise Him! Praise Him!
Jesus is a friend of mine
Praise Him!

2 Jesus died to set us free
Praise Him!
Jesus died to set us free
Praise Him!
Praise Him! Praise Him!
Jesus died to set us free
Praise Him!

3 Jesus is the King of Kings
Praise Him!
Jesus is the King of Kings
Praise Him!
Praise Him! Praise Him!
Jesus is the King of Kings
Praise Him!

108 Jesus knows

S.B. Daleburn

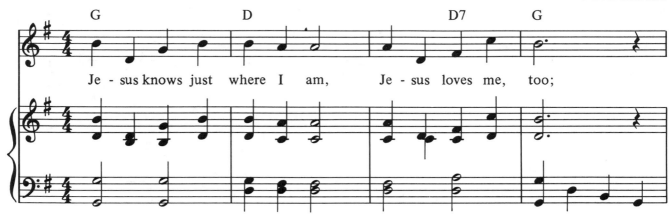

Je - sus knows just where I am, Je - sus loves me, too;

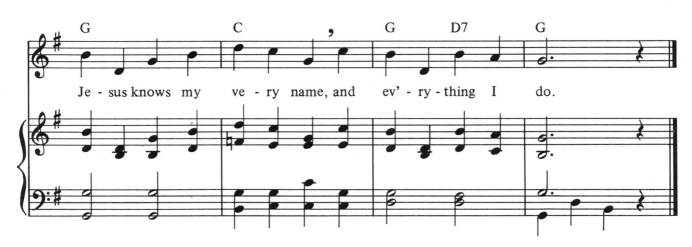

Je - sus knows my ve - ry name, and ev' - ry - thing I do.

Jesus knows just where I am,
Jesus loves me, too;
Jesus knows my very name,
and ev'rything I do.

109 Jesus is pleased

Marie H. Frost
arr. Phil Burt

1 Jesus is pleased when I share what I have,
   share what I have, share what I have.
   Jesus is pleased when I share what I have,
   so that's what I will do.

2 Jesus wants me to learn more about Him,
   more about Him, more about Him.
   Jesus wants me to learn more about Him,
   so that's what I will do.

110 Jesus is the best friend

J. Sibley

E.M. Stephenson

Je - sus is the best Friend, I know that He loves me._____ He helps me when I'm feel - ing sad, I'm glad that He loves me.

1 Jesus is the best Friend,
   I know that He loves me.
   He helps me when I'm feeling sad,
   I'm glad that He loves me.

2 Jesus is the best Friend,
   I know that He loves me.
   He helps me when I've done wrong things,
   I'm glad that He loves me.

3 Jesus is the best Friend,
   I know that He loves me.
   He helps me when I feel alone,
   I'm glad that He loves me.

4 Jesus is the best Friend,
   I know that He loves me.
   He helps me when I'm happy too,
   I'm glad that He loves me.

111 Jesus is the Son of God

Phil Burt

1 Jesus is the Son of God,
   Son of God, Son of God.
   Jesus is the Son of God,
   He healed the crippled man.

2 He made the blind man see.

3 He made the dead girl live.

112 Jesus is the Son of God, Praise His name

Steve Tippett

Capo 3

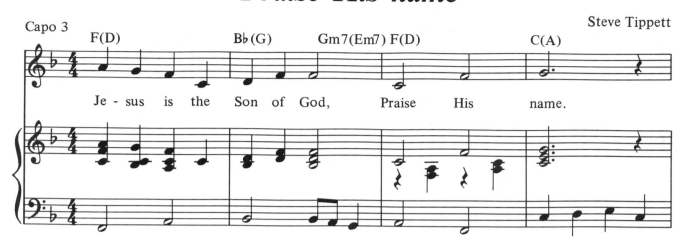

Je - sus is the Son of God, Praise His name.

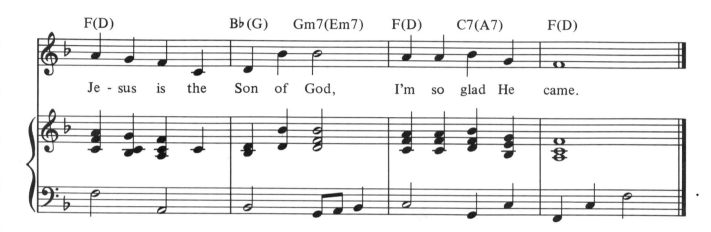

Je - sus is the Son of God, I'm so glad He came.

1 Jesus is the Son of God,
   Praise His name.
   Jesus is the Son of God,
   I'm so glad He came.

2 Jesus Christ was born a King

3 Jesus died but rose again

4 Jesus Christ will never change

5 Jesus said He would come back,
   Praise His name.
   Jesus said He would come back,
   Then as King He'll reign.

Additional words V2-5. © 1990 Greg Leavers

113 Jesus, let Your love flow

Joan Robinson
arr. Phil Burt

Je - sus, let Your love flow, let Your love flow through me. Je - sus, let Your love flow, let Your love flow through me. I want to show it and to give it to ev' - ry-one I see. I want to

show it and to give it to ev' - ry - one — I see.

1 Jesus, let Your love flow,
   let Your love flow thro' me.
   Jesus, let Your love flow,
   let Your love flow thro' me.
   I want to show it and to give it
   to everyone I see.
   I want to show it and to give it
   to everyone I see.

2 Jesus, let Your joy flow . . .

3 Jesus, let Your peace flow . . .

114 Jesus, Jesus

W.J. Kirkpatrick

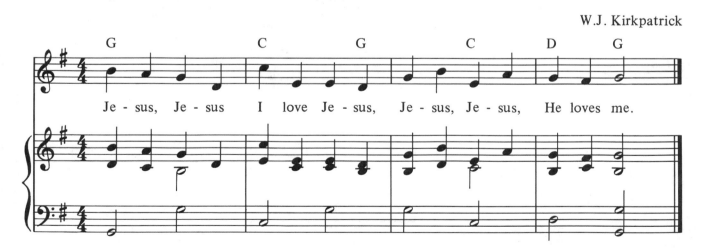

Je - sus, Je - sus I love Je - sus, Je - sus, Je - sus, He loves me.

Jesus, Jesus, I love Jesus,
Jesus, Jesus, He loves me.

115 Jesus' love is very wonderful

H.W. Rattle

arr. Phil Burt

So wide, you can't get round it, O won-der-ful love!

Jesus' love is very wonderful,
Jesus' love is very wonderful,
Jesus' love is very wonderful,
O wonderful love!
So high, you can't get over it,
so low, you can't get under it,
so wide, you can't get round it,
O wonderful love!

116 Jesus loves me

William B. Bradbury
arr. Phil Burt

1. Je - sus loves me, this I know, for the Bi - ble tells me so.
Lit - tle ones to Him be - long, they are weak but He is strong.
Yes, Je - sus loves me. Yes, Je - sus loves me,
Yes, Je - sus loves me, the Bi - ble tells me so.

1 Jesus loves me this I know,
  for the Bible tells me so.
  Little ones to Him belong,
  they are weak but He is strong.

  Yes, Jesus loves me.
  Yes, Jesus loves me.
  Yes, Jesus loves me,
  the Bible tells me so.

2 Jesus loves me when I'm good,
  when I do the things I should.
  Jesus loves me when I'm bad,
  though it makes Him very sad.
      Yes, Jesus . . .

3 Jesus loves me, He who died,
  heaven's gates to open wide.
  He will wash away my sin,
  let this little child come in.
      Yes, Jesus . . .

4 Boys and girls across the seas,
  Jesus loves as well as me;
  so our little friends are they,
  and with us they all can say:
      Yes, Jesus . . .

117 Jesus prayed in Gethsemane

Greg Leavers

1 Jesus prayed in Gethsemane,
Jesus prayed in Gethsemane,
Jesus prayed in Gethsemane,
'Father I will obey You.'

2 Why did Jesus look so sad?
Why did Jesus look so sad?
Why did Jesus look so sad?
He knew that He must die.

3 Peter, James and John were there,
Peter, James and John were there,
Peter, James and John were there,
but all they did was sleep.

4 A great big crowd with Judas came,
a great big crowd with Judas came,
a great big crowd with Judas came,
he showed them who was Jesus.

5 Jesus didn't deserve to die,
Jesus didn't deserve to die,
Jesus didn't deserve to die,
He died because He loves me.

118 Jesus teach me

Phyllis J. Warfel

1 Jesus, teach me how to love, love others,
Teach me how to love, love others.
Teach me how to love, love others.
Then show that love through me.

2 Jesus teach me how to forgive others.
Teach me how to forgive others.
Teach me how to forgive others.
Then show forgiveness through me.

119 Jesus was born to Mary

J. Watson

J. Mackenzie

Je -sus was born to Ma - ry, a ba - by weak and small.

Why did He come from Hea - ven? Be - cause He loved us all.

1 Jesus was born to Mary,
a baby weak and small.
Why did He come from Heaven?
Because He loved us all.

2 Jesus became a teacher,
healing with His touch.
Why did He work for others?
Because He loved so much.

3 Jesus was put in prison,
but nothing wrong He'd done.
Why did He die so sadly?
Because He loved each one.

4 Jesus the King is living,
His death was not the end.
He died because He loved us,
He lives to be our friend.

120 Let us love one another

Norman L. Starks

Let us love one another, love one another,
growing and caring more each day.
O let us love one another, love one another,
learning to walk in Jesus' way.

121 Jesus will never, ever

Greg Leavers
arr. Phil Burt

Je - sus will ne - ver, e - ver, no not ev - er,

ne - ver ev - er change. He will al - ways, al - ways,

that's for all days, al - ways be the same, so as

Son of God and King of kings He will for - ev - er reign,

yes - ter - day to - day for - ev - er, Je - sus is the same.

Yes - ter - day to - day for - ev - er, Je - sus is the same.

Jesus will never, ever,
no not ever, never ever change.
He will always, always,
that's for all days,
always be the same;
so as Son of God and
King of kings
He will forever reign.
Yesterday today forever,
Jesus is the same.
Yesterday today forever,
Jesus is the same.

122 Joseph

Joan Robinson

Joseph was sold as a slave, and later was thrown into prison, but God helped him be very brave, because he had done nothing wrong. *For God*

Chorus

1 Joseph was sold as a slave,
  and later was thrown into prison,
  but God helped him be very brave,
  because he had done nothing wrong
  For God knows, yes God knows,
  God knows the truth; for God knows,
  yes God knows, God knows the truth.

2 Sometimes when things all go wrong,
  and the punishment seems so unfair,
  remember the words of this song,
  then talk to God. He's always there.
  For God knows, yes God knows,
  God knows the truth; for God knows,
  yes God knows, God knows the truth.

123 Joy is the flag

Anon
arr. Phil Burt

Joy is the flag flown high from the cas - tle of my heart, from the cas - tle of my heart, from the cas - tle of my heart. Joy is the flag flown high from the cas - tle of my heart, when the King is in resi - den - ce there._____ So let it

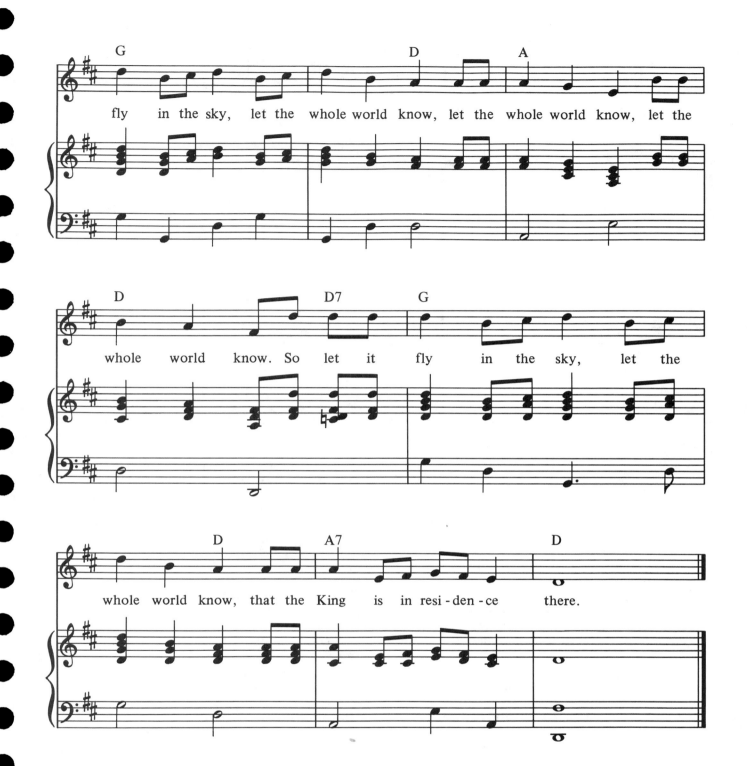

Joy is the flag flown high from the castle of my heart,
from the castle of my heart, from the castle of my heart.
Joy is the flag flown high from the castle of my heart,
when the King is in residence there.
So let it fly in the sky, let the whole world know,
let the whole world know, let the whole world know.
So let it fly in the sky, let the whole world know,
that the King is in residence there.

124 Little baby Moses

D.B. Martin

E.M. Stephenson

Lit - tle ba - by Mo - ses roc - king on the wat - er.

Hush! Hush! Hide a -way, here comes Phar -aoh's daugh - ter!

1 Little baby Moses
   rocking on the water.
   Hush! Hush! Hide away,
   here comes Pharaoh's daughter!

2 Pharaoh's daughter takes him
   in her royal hand.
   Weep not, Miriam,
   this is what God planned.

3 In the court of Egypt
   growing wise and clever,
   hears God telling him,
   'You are mine, forever.'

4 'Lead away My people
   over desert sand,
   long years wandering
   to the Promised Land.'

5 'Tell them they must love Me,
   tell them to obey,
   in cloud and fire before them
   I will lead the way.'

125 Lord I want to sing

Greg Leavers

Anon
arr. Phil Burt

1 Lord I want to sing a great big thank you,
   Lord I want to sing a great big thank you,
   Lord I want to sing a great big thank you,
   for loving me the way You do.

2 Lord I want to shout a loud 'Hallelujah'!

3 Lord I want to whisper a quiet 'I love You'!

126 Lord, You are brilliant

Greg Leavers

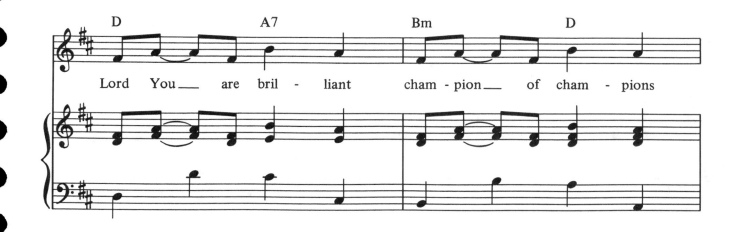

Lord You___ are bril - liant cham - pion___ of cham - pions

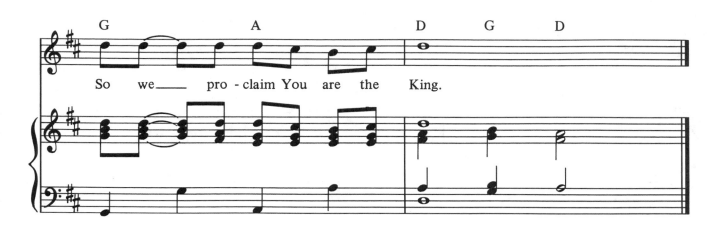

So we___ pro - claim You are the King.

1 Lord You are brilliant, champion of champions,
   to You our thanks and praise we bring.
   You made all the world, no-one's as great as You,
   You know everything and all Your words are true,
   Lord You are brilliant, champion of champions.
   So we proclaim You are the King.

2 Lord You are brilliant, champion of champions,
   to You our thanks and praise we bring.
   You see everything, all that we say and do,
   You're incredible, no-one loves us like You,
   Lord You are brilliant, champion of champions.
   So we proclaim You are the King.

127 Mister Noah built an ark

arr. Phil Burt

Mis - ter No - ah built an ark, the peo - ple thought it such a lark. Mis - ter No - ah plead - ed so but in - to the ark they would not go. *Down came the rain in tor - rents (splish, splash), down came the rain in tor - rents (splish, splash),*

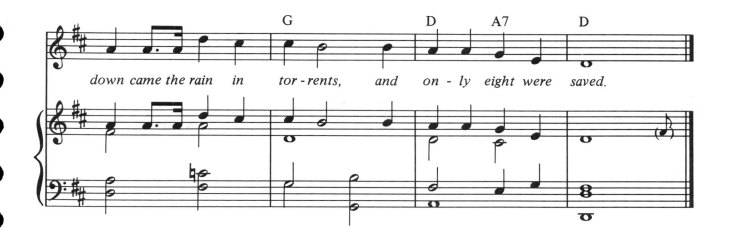

down came the rain in tor-rents, and on-ly eight were saved.

1   Mister Noah built an ark,
    the people thought it such a lark.
    Mister Noah pleaded so
    but into the ark they would not go.

    Down came the rain in torrents   *(splish, splash),*
    down came the rain in torrents   *(splish, splash),*   spoken
    down came the rain in torrents,
    and only eight were saved.

2   The animals went in two by two,
    elephant, giraffe and kangaroo.
    All were safely stowed away
    on that great and awful day.

    Down came the rain in torrents   *(splish, splash),*
    down came the rain in torrents   *(splish, splash),*   spoken
    down came the rain in torrents,
    and only eight were saved.

    (Then to tune of chorus)

    Whenever you see a rainbow,
    whenever you see a rainbow,
    whenever you see a rainbow,
    remember God is love.

128 Moses, Moses

Joan Robinson
arr. Phil Burt

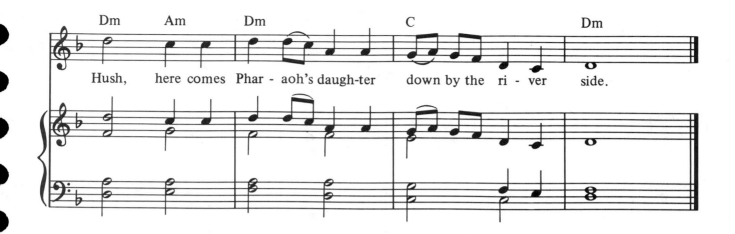

1 Moses, Moses who's going to find you
down by the river side?
Moses, Moses who's going to find you
down by the river side?
Hush, here comes Pharaoh's daughter
bathing in the water, bathing in the water.
Hush, here comes Pharaoh's daughter
down by the river side.

2 Pharaoh's daughter takes little Moses
though he is a Jew.
Pharaoh's daughter takes little Moses
though he is a Jew.
He is raised an Egyptian Prince
living in a palace, living in a palace.
He is raised an Egyptian Prince
though he is a Jew.

129 Mutter, mutter, moan and splutter

Words & Music
Greg Leavers

Mut - ter, mut - ter, moan and splut - ter, when they heard what Je - sus said;

whinge - ing, whin - ing tem - pers ri - sing, when they saw what Je - sus did.

1 Mutter, mutter, moan and splutter,
 when they heard what Jesus said;
 whingeing, whining, tempers rising,
 when they saw what Jesus did.

2 Grumble, grumble, groan and mumble,
 how the Pharisees went on!
 Then complaining, moaning, saying
 'How dare He say He is God's Son.'

3 Lame men walking, dumb folk talking,
 miracles they saw Him do.
 Jesus did this through God's power
 showing all He said was true.

130 Not one, not two, not three, but four

Greg Leavers
arr. Phil Burt

1 Not one, not two, not three but four men,
  couldn't get anywhere near the door when
  they saw steps up to the roof. Then
  made a great big hole to let the sick man down.

2 One, two, three, four, five, six, seven,
  Jesus said, 'Your sin's forgiven.'
  Heard folk murmuring so said to him,
  'Now stand up, pick up your bed, and then go home.'

3 Three, four, five, six, seven, eight, nine, ten,
  this is how the Saviour works when
  we bring people who need help, then
  He can change their lives so they can follow Him.

131 My God is so big

arr. Phil Burt

Lyrics: My God is so big, so strong and so mighty, there's no-thing that He can-not do. The ri-vers are His, the moun-tains are His, the stars are His han-di-work too. My

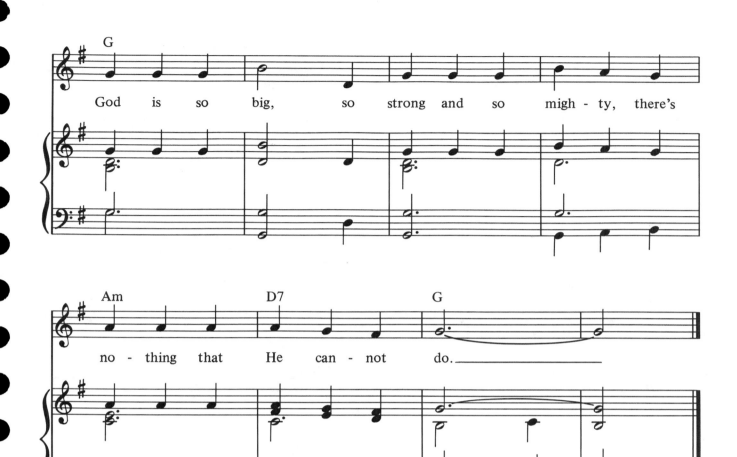

God is so big, so strong and so migh-ty, there's no-thing that He can-not do.

1 My God is so big, so strong and so mighty,⎫
  there's nothing that He cannot do.   ⎬ *repeat*
  The rivers are His, the mountains are His,
  the stars are His handiwork too.
  My God is so big, so strong and so mighty,
  there's nothing that He cannot do.

2 My God is so big, so strong and so mighty,⎫
  there's nothing that He cannot do.   ⎬ *repeat*
  He's called you to live, for Him ev'ry day,
  in all that you say and you do.
  My God is so big, so strong and so mighty,
  He can do all things through you.

132 Oh no! The wine's all gone

Greg Leavers

Oh no! The wine's all gone, how can the wed-ding feast

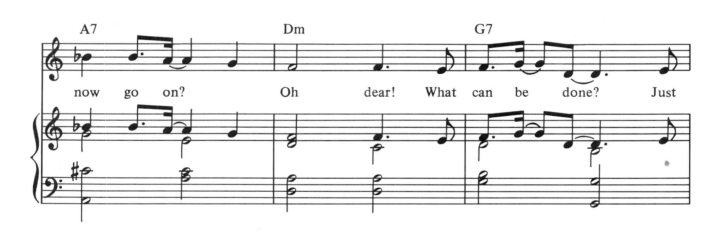

now go on? Oh dear! What can be done? Just

li - sten to Je - sus, Ma - ry's Son. Oh yes! We'll

Oh no! The wine's all gone,
how can the wedding feast now go on?
Oh dear! What can be done?
Just listen to Jesus, Mary's Son,
Oh yes! We'll do what He says,
fill the stone jars with water that's fresh.
Oh my! They're pouring it out.
What? Wine? That's the miracle! Without a doubt!

133 Oh! Oh! Oh! how good is the Lord

Anon
arr. Phil Burt

Oh! Oh! Oh! how good is the Lord. Oh! Oh! Oh! how good is the Lord.

Oh! Oh! Oh! how good is the Lord, I ne-ver will for-get what He has

done for me. He gives me sal-va-tion, how good is the Lord. He

gives me sal-va-tion, how good is the Lord. He gives me sal-va-tion, how

good is the Lord. I ne-ver will for-get what He has done for me.

Oh! Oh! Oh! how good is the Lord.
Oh! Oh! Oh! how good is the Lord.
Oh! Oh! Oh! how good is the Lord,
I never will forget what He has done for me.

1 He gives me salvation, how good is the Lord.
He gives me salvation, how good is the Lord.
He gives me salvation, how good is the Lord,
I never will forget what He has done for me.
  Oh! Oh! Oh! . . .

2 He gives me His blessings . . .
  Oh! Oh! Oh! . . .

Other suitable verses may be added.

He gives me His Spirit . . .
  Oh! Oh! Oh! . . .

He gives us our friends . . .
  Oh! Oh! Oh! . . .

He gives me His healing . . .
  Oh! Oh! Oh! . . .

He gives us each other . . .
  Oh! Oh! Oh! . . .

He gives us the harvest
  Oh! Oh! Oh! . . .

134 One and two and three and four

Greg Leavers

Capo 3

One and two and three and four, counting sheep in through the door, fifty one and fifty two, one is lost, what shall I do?

he was lost but now is—— found.—— So it's

nine - ty eight, nine - ty nine, (click fingers) one hun - dred.—— Yes it's

nine - ty eight, nine - ty nine, (click fingers) one hun - dred!——

One and two and three and four,
counting sheep in through the door,
fifty one and fifty two,
one is lost, what shall I do?
Ninety eight and ninety nine,
I will search until I find,
I will keep on looking just because I care.
There he is caught in some thorns way over there,
he was lost but now is found.
So it's ninety eight, ninety nine, (click fingers) one hundred;
Yes it's ninety eight, ninety nine, (click fingers) one hundred.

135 Over the world this Christmas

Joan Robinson
arr. Phil Burt

O - ver the world this Christ - mas morn the mes - sage rings

out that Je - sus is born that Je - sus is born that

Je - sus is born the mes - sage rings out that Je - sus is born.

1 Over the world this Christmas morn
   the message rings out that Jesus is born,
   that Jesus is born, that Jesus is born,
   the message rings out that Jesus is born.

2 Over the world and over the sea
   the message rings out that Jesus loves me,
   that Jesus loves me, that Jesus loves me,
   the message rings out that Jesus loves me.

3 Over the world I know it is true
   the message rings out that Jesus loves you,
   that Jesus loves you, that Jesus loves you,
   the message rings out that Jesus loves you.

4 Over the world let your voices sing
   the message rings out that Jesus is King,
   that Jesus is King, that Jesus is King,
   the message rings out that Jesus is King.

136 One day a man was walking

Mary Kay Bottens

1. One day a man was walk-ing down to Jer-i-cho, when sud-den-ly some thieves rushed down up-on the road. They stripped him of his rai-ment and they wound-ed him. Then hur-ried off to car-ry on their lives of sin.

1 One day a man was walking down to Jericho,
  when suddenly some thieves rushed down upon the road.
  They stripped him of his raiment and they wounded him.
  Then hurried off to carry on their lives of sin.

2 And then there came a certain priest along that way,
  but he just passed the man without a word to say,
  and likewise came a Levite who was filled with pride,
  and he, too, hurried over to the other side.

3 When who but a Samaritan should come along,
  he had compassion on him; he knew right from wrong.
  He bound his wounds and lifted him up on his beast;
  he paid for lodging for him till his pain had ceased.

4 And so this is the question, which one of these three
  was then the kind of neighbour you and I should be?
  Of course, the answer's clear - the good Samaritan.
  So follow his example - it's the Master's plan.

137 One day I might

Greg Leavers
arr. Phil Burt

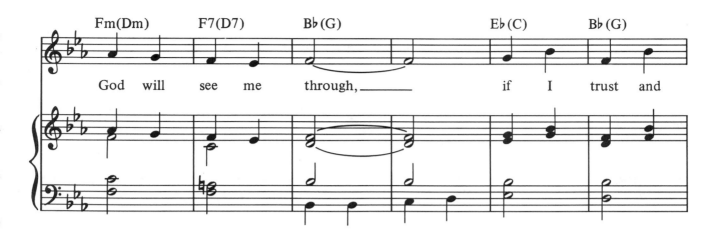

God will see me through, _____ if I trust and

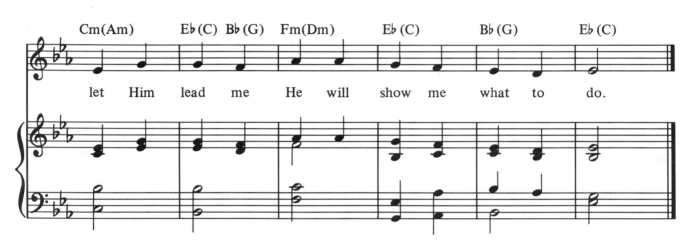

let Him lead me He will show me what to do.

One day I might drive a police car,
dee-daa dee-daa, dee-daa, dee.
One day I might be a teacher,
'Now be quiet and do your work,'
but I know what ever happens
God will see me through,
if I trust and let Him lead me.
He will show me what to do.

138 One, two, three, Jesus loves me

Lisa Mazak

One, two, three, Je - sus loves me. One, two,

Je - sus loves you. 1. Three, four, He loves you more

than you've ev - er been loved be - fore. 2. Five, six, seven, we're

go - ing to heav'n. Eight, nine, it's tru - ly di - vine.

3. Nine, ten, it's time to end; But in - stead we'll

sing it a - gain. there's no time to sing it a - gain.

One, two, three, Jesus loves me.
One, two, Jesus loves you

1 Three, four, He loves you more
   than you've ever been loved before.
      One, two, three, . . .

2 Five, six, seven, we're going to heav'n.
   Eight, nine, it's truly divine.
      One, two, three, . . .

3 Nine, ten, its time to end;
   But instead we'll sing it again
   (There's no time to sing it again).
      One, two, three, . . .

139 Only a boy called David

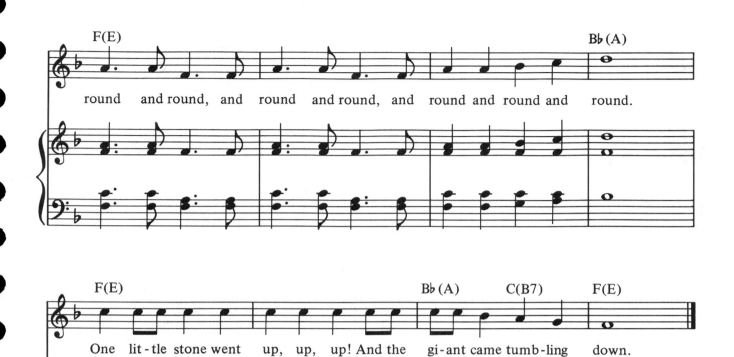

round and round, and round and round, and round and round and round.

One lit-tle stone went up, up, up! And the gi-ant came tumb-ling down.

Only a boy called David,
only a rippling brook;
Only a boy called David,
five little stones he took.
Then, one little stone went in the sling,
and the sling went round and round,
one little stone went in the sling,
and the sling went round and round,
round and round, and round and round,
and round and round and round.
One little stone went up, up, up!
And the giant came tumbling down.

140 Praise God

Sarah Eberle

Praise God with a shout:(Shout) the Lord, He is God!
Praise Him with a clap: (Clap) clap — clap—clap—clap
Praise God with a song: (Sing) the Lord, He is God!
Praise Him every way that you can.

141 Praise Him, praise Him, all you little children

1 Praise Him praise Him, all you little children,
God is love, God is love.
Praise Him, praise Him, all you little children,
God is love, God is love.

2 Love Him, love Him, all you little children,
God is love, God is love.
Love Him, love Him, all you little children,
God is love, God is love.

3 Thank Him, thank Him, all you little children,
God is love, God is love.
Thank Him, thank Him, all you little children,
God is love, God is love.

142 Praise Him, praise Him, praise Him in the morning

arr. Phil Burt

1 Praise Him, praise Him,
  praise Him in the morning,
  praise Him in the noontime,
  praise Him, praise Him,
  praise Him as the sun goes down.

2 Thank Him . . . *etc.*

3 Love Him . . . *etc.*

4 Serve Him . . . *etc.*

143 Praise King Jesus

D. Parsons

1 Praise King Jesus
   riding into town,
   riding on a donkey,
   throw your jackets down!
   Sing hosanna!
   Wave your branches!
   Praise King Jesus,
   riding into town.

2 Praise King Jesus,
   He's alive today.
   He's alive for ever,
   sing a loud Hooray!
   Alleluia!
   We will love Him.
   Praise King Jesus,
   He's alive today.

144 Praise the Lord with the sound of a drum

Briskly

Joan Robinson
arr. Phil Burt

Praise the Lord with the sound of a drum. Praise the Lord with the sound of a drum. Praise the Lord with the sound of a drum. Praise the Lord with the sound of a drum.

Rum tiddly tum tum tum tum tum, tum (crash)

tap tap tap tap shake shake shake shake shake ting!

Rhythm ♫♪ ♫♪ ♫

1 Praise the Lord with the sound of a drum.
  Praise the Lord with the sound of a drum.
  Praise the Lord with the sound of a drum.
  Rum tiddly tum tum tum tum tum.

2 Praise the Lord with the cymbal crash.
  Praise the Lord with the cymbal crash.
  Praise the Lord with the cymbal crash.
  Rum tiddly tum tum tum, tum, tum *(crash.)*

3 Praise the Lord with the tambourine.
  Praise the Lord with the tambourine.
  Praise the Lord with the tambourine.
  Rum tiddly tum tum tum tum, tap tap tap tap

4 Praise the Lord with the maracas.
  Praise the Lord with the maracas.
  Praise the Lord with the maracas.
  Rum tiddly tum tum tum tum, shake shake shake shake.

5 Praise the Lord with the triangle.
  Praise the Lord with the triangle.
  Praise the Lord with the triangle.
  Rum tiddly tum tum tum tum, shake ting!

6 Praise the Lord with dancing feet.
  Praise the Lord with dancing feet.
  Praise the Lord with dancing feet.
  Rum tiddly tum tum tum tum.

145 Praise and thanksgiving

(3 part round)

arr. Greg Leavers

Praise and thanksgiving let everyone bring,
unto our Father for every good thing!
All together joyfully sing.

Melody can be sung as a round instead of playing the harmony. Guitar chords are only for the round.

Arr. © 1991 Greg Leavers

146 Rocking, rocking

I.M. Buttle

1 Rocking, rocking,
  on the blue sea,
  lay Peter's little brown boat.

2 Sailing, sailing,
  over the sea,
  went Peter's little brown boat.

3 Fishing, fishing,
  in the blue sea,
  were strong men in Peter's brown boat.

4 Helping, helping,
  men of the sea,
  was Jesus in Peter's brown boat.

5 Resting, resting,
  out on the sea,
  lay Jesus in Peter's brown boat.

147 See the star

Alice Koerner
arr. Phil Burt

Capo 3

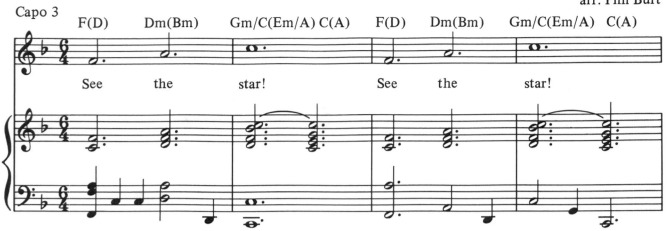

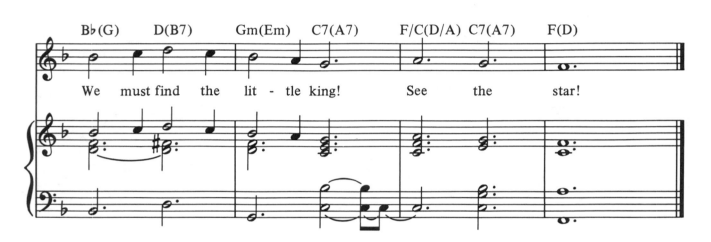

1 See the star!
  See the star!
  We must find the little king!
  See the star!

2 Where is He?
  Where is He?
  We are come to worship Him.
  Where is He?

3 Let us kneel,
  Let us kneel.
  God has sent His only Son;
  Let us kneel.

148 See the turtle

Phil Burt

Capo 5 (Am)

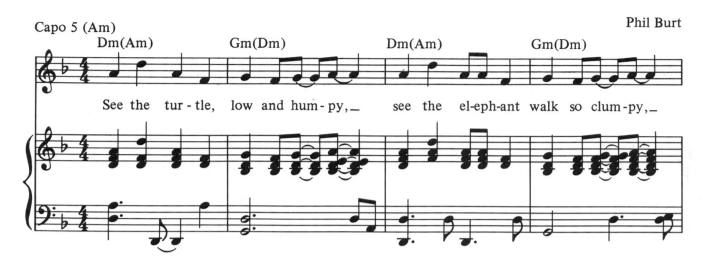

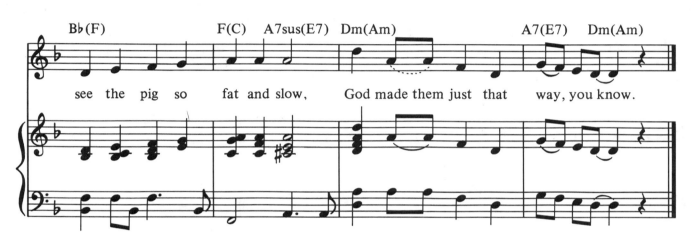

See the turtle, low and humpy,
  *(bend over, move hand in a
  semicircle, just above floor)*
see the elephant walk so clumpy,
  (lift feet slowly, as if very heavy)
see the pig, so fat and slow,
  (round out tummy with hands)
God *(point finger upward)* made them just that way, you know.

See the squeaky mouse so small,
  (crouch down and indicate size with fingers)
so different from the horse that's tall;
  (reach high on tiptoe)
see the robin flap his wings,
  (flap arms)
thank You, God, who made all things.
  (bow head, fold hands in prayer)

Music © 1990 Phil Burt

Words Copyright control

149 Shalōm, my friend

Capo 5

Michael Lehr

Michael Metcalf

Shalöm, my friend, shalöm, my friend,
shalöm, shalöm.
Till we meet again, till we meet again,
shalöm, shalöm.

150 Someone's brought a loaf of bread
(The harvest table)

arr. Phil Burt

Some-one's brought a loaf of bread, some-one's brought a loaf of bread,

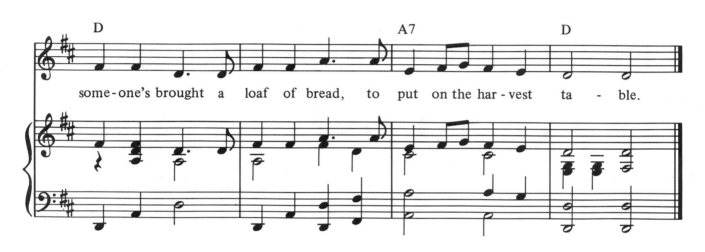

some-one's brought a loaf of bread, to put on the har-vest ta - ble.

1 Someone's brought a loaf of bread,
   someone's brought a loaf of bread,
   someone's brought a loaf of bread,
   to put on the harvest table.

2 Someone's brought a jar of jam,
   someone's brought a jar of jam,
   someone's brought a jar of jam,
   to put on the harvest table.

Other verses as desired

Last verse: Thank You Lord for all Your gifts,
   thank You Lord for all Your gifts,
   thank You Lord for all Your gifts,
   to put on the harvest table.

151 Sing and celebrate
(Christmas)

Greg Leavers

Capo 1

Chorus F(E)

Sing and — ce - le brate (sing and — ce - le brate), God gave Je - sus,—

Eb (D)   F(E)

(God gave Je - sus),— Light for all — the world (Light for all — the world),

Bb(A)   Eb(D)   C(B7)

born at Christ - mas — (born at Christ - mas — time). _____

last time to %.   *Verse* Gm(F#m)   Bb(A)   F(E)   C(B7)

— Je - sus our light,— shines bright,— what de-light;

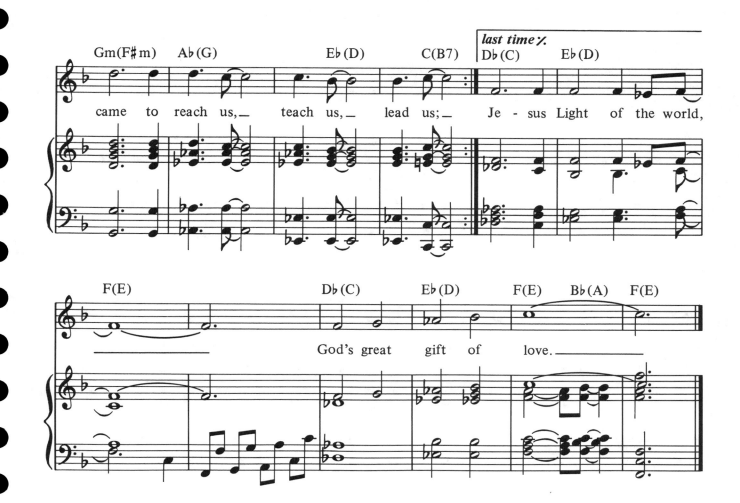

Chorus:

Sing and celebrate (sing and celebrate),
God gave Jesus (God gave Jesus),
Light for all the world (Light for all the world),
born Born at Christmas (born at Christmas time).

1. Jesus, our light,
   shines bright,
   what delight;
   came to reach us,
   teach us,
   lead us;

   Sing and . . .

2. God so loved us,
   gave us,
   Jesus;
   Lord we thank You,
   love You,
   serve You;

   Sing and . . .

ending: Jesus, Light of the world,
         God's great gift of love.

152 Sing and celebrate
(Easter)

Greg Leavers

Sing and celebrate (sing and celebrate), Christ is risen (Christ is risen), champion of the world (champion of the world), lives for ever (lives for ever more).

God so loved us, gave us, Jesus,

chorus; Sing and celebrate (Sing and celebrate),
        Christ is risen (Christ is risen),
        Champion of the world (Champion of the world),
        Lives for ever (Lives for evermore).

1 God so loved us,
  gave us,
  Jesus;
  Died on Calvary,
  set free,
  you and me;

Sing and . . .

2 Jesus our friend,
  died then,
  rose again;
  Lord we love You,
  thank You,
  praise You;

Sing and . . .

ending: Jesus died for the world,
         God's great gift of love.

Singing sequence: chorus
              verse one
              chorus
              chorus
              verse two
              chorus
              ending

153 Sometimes I'm naughty

Greg Leavers
arr. Phil Burt

Some times I'm naugh ty, I know I've been bad, _____ I say such un-kind things and make peo-ple sad.

Chorus Fa - ther, _____ I know I've done wrong, Lord please for - give me I pray. _____

I want to say,— I want to say,—

I am so sor - ry — Lord.————

1 Sometimes I'm naughty
  I know I've been bad;
  I say such unkind things
  and make people sad.
      Father I know I've done wrong,
      Lord, please forgive me, I pray.
      I want to say,
      I want to say,
      that I'm so sorry, Lord.

2 I'm rude to my family,
  I want my own way.
  I don't show them kindness
  or do what they say.
      Father . . .

3 In love You forgive me,
  I'm glad I'm Your child.
  Your Spirit lives in me
  to change me inside.
      Father help me today,
      Help me to please You, I pray.
      I want to say.
      I want to say.
      how much I love You, Lord.

154 Sometimes problems

Greg Leavers
arr. Phil Burt

Some-times pro-blems can be BIG, some-times pro-blems can be *small,* but it does-n't real-ly mat-ter for what-ev-er the size,— Je-sus wants to help us with them all, so we can tell Him all a-bout it.

Trust His word don't doubt it, don't be a - fraid:

DON'T BE A - FRAID, just (1, 2, 3, 4) be - lieve.

Sometimes problems can be BIG,
sometimes problems can be *small,*
but it doesn't really matter
for whatever the size,
Jesus wants to help us with them all, so we can
tell Him all about it.
Trust His word don't doubt it,
don't be afraid:
DON'T BE AFRAID,
just (1—2—3—4) believe.

Some days I wake up feeling GLAD
some days I wake up feeling *sad,*
but it doesn't really matter
for whatever the day
Jesus wants to help us through them all, He's promised
He will never leave us,
He will not forsake us,
don't be dismayed,
DON'T BE AFRAID,
just (1—2—3—4) believe.

Words in Capitals spoken with a loud voice
Words in Italics spoken quietly

155 Sorry Lord

Greg Leavers
arr. Phil Burt

Sor - ry Lord, for all the things that I've done wrong, please make me clean, for - give my sin, I want to fol - low You.

1 Sorry Lord, for all the things
that I've done wrong, please
make me clean, forgive my sin,
I want to follow You.

2 Thank You Lord, for dying on
the cross to save me,
fill my heart for my new start,
please come and live in me.

3 I love You, please help me Lord
to follow closely
from today in every way,
please make me more like You.

156(i) Thank You for the world so sweet

1st tune

Anon
arr. Phil Burt

Thank You for the world so sweet.
Thank You for the food we eat.
Thank You for the birds that sing.
Thank You God for everything.

156(ii) Thank You for the world so sweet

2nd tune

arr. Phil Burt

Thank You for the world so sweet *(clap clap)*.
Thank You for the food we eat*   *(yum yum)*.
Thank You for the birds that sing-a-ling-a-ling.**
Thank You God for every thing *(Amen)*.

* Rub tummy
** Make action for birds singing

157 Thank You, Lord, for giving us this day

Jenna Lusby Houp

Thank You, Lord, for giving us this day.
Thank You, Lord, for being our friend.
Thank You, Lord for showing us the way,
through Jesus. Amen.

158 Thank You for the love

Andy Silver

Thank You for the love that our mums give to us each day,

thank You for the help and the care that they bring our way.

Lord, we thank You for eve - ry - thing they do,

show us how to help them too. Show us how to live, teach - ing

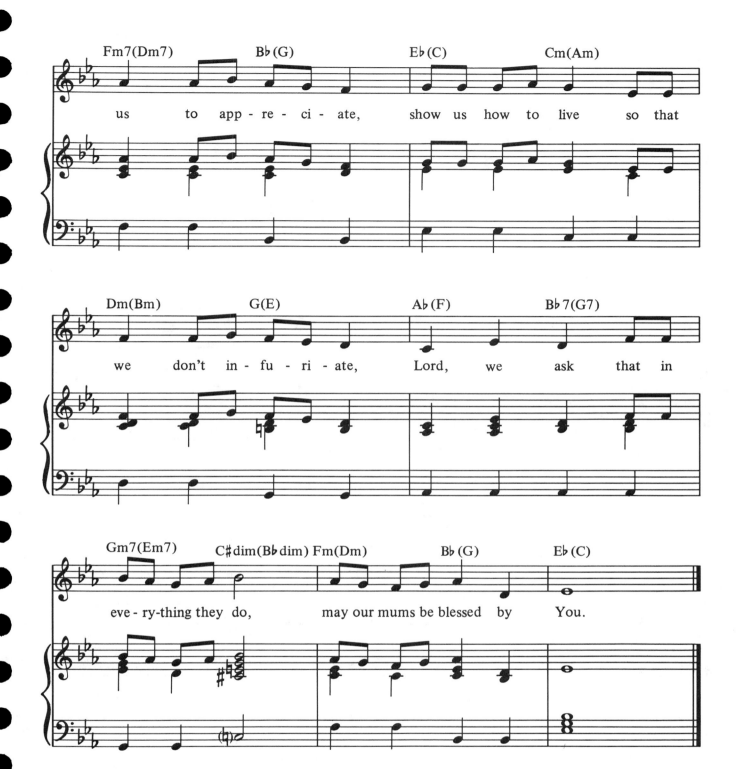

Thank You for the love that our mums give to us each day,
thank You for the help and the care that they bring our way.
Lord, we thank You for everything they do,
show us how to help them too.
Show us how to live, teaching us to appreciate,
show us how to live so that we don't infuriate,
Lord, we ask that in everything they do,
may our mums be blessed by You.

159 Thank You Jesus

Unknown
arr. Roland Fudge

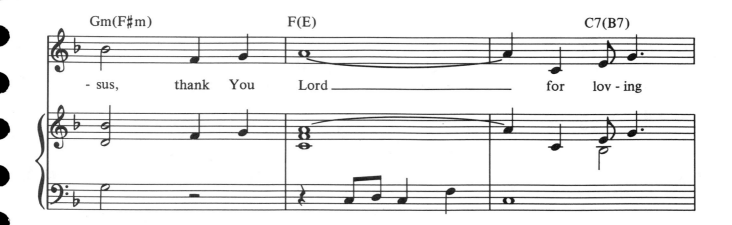

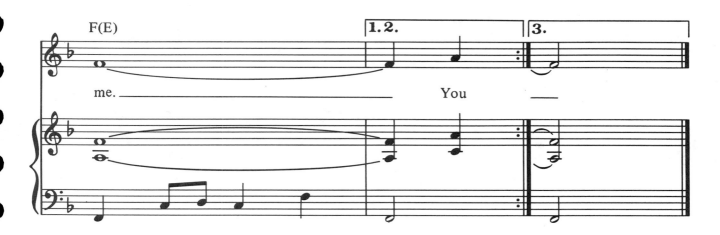

1 Thank You Jesus, thank You Jesus,
   thank You Lord for loving me.
   Thank You Jesus, thank You Jesus,
   thank You Lord for loving me.

2 You went to Calvary, there You died for me,
   thank You Lord for loving me.
   You went to Calvary, there You died for me,
   thank You Lord for loving me.

3 You rose up from the grave, to me new life You gave,
   thank You Lord for loving me.
   You rose up from the grave, to me new life You gave,
   thank You Lord for loving me.

4 You're coming back again, and we with You shall reign,
   thank You Lord for loving me.
   You're coming back again, and we with You shall reign,
   thank You Lord for loving me.

160 Thank You, Lord, for this fine day

Diane Davis Andrew

Capo 1

Thank ___ You, Lord, for this fine day, thank ___ You, Lord, for

this fine day, thank ___ You, Lord, for this fine day,

right ___ where we are. Al - le - lu - ia,

praise the Lord! Al - le - lu - ia, praise the Lord! Al -

le - lu - ia, praise the Lord! Right— where we are.

1 Thank You, Lord, for this fine day,
   thank You, Lord, for this fine day,
   thank You, Lord, for this fine day,
   right where we are.

   Alleluia, praise the Lord!
   Alleluia, praise the Lord!
   Alleluia, praise the Lord!
   Right where we are.

2 Thank You, Lord, for loving us,
   thank You, Lord, for loving us,
   thank You, Lord, for loving us,
   right where we are.
       Alleluia, . . .

3 Thank You, Lord, for giving us peace,
   thank You, Lord, for giving us peace,
   thank You, Lord, for giving us peace,
   right where we are.
       Alleluia, . . .

4 Thank You, Lord, for setting us free,
   thank You, Lord, for setting us free,
   thank You, Lord, for setting us free,
   right where we are.
       Alleluia, . . .

5 Thank You, Lord, for games to play,
   thank You, Lord, for games to play,
   thank You, Lord, for games to play,
   right where we are.
       Alleluia, . . .

161 The best book to read

P. Bilhorn

The best book to read is the Bi - ble, the best book to read is the Bi - ble; if you read it ev-'ry day it will help you on your way, oh, the best book to read is the Bi - ble.

1 The best book to read is the Bible,
the best book to read is the Bible;
if you read it every day
it will help you on your way,
oh, the best book to read is the Bible.

2 The best friend to have is Jesus,
the best friend to have is Jesus;
He will hear me when I call;
He will keep me lest I fall,
oh, the best friend to have is Jesus.

3 The best thing to do is to trust Him,
the best thing to do is to trust Him;
and if you on Him depend,
He will keep you to the end,
oh, the best thing to do is to trust Him.

162 The Bible tells

St. Peter
Betty McCollough

A.R. Reinagle

The Bi - ble tells of God's great plan for peo - ple e - very -

where, that all should learn to live in love and in His king-dom share.

1 The Bible tells of God's great plan
for people everywhere,
that all should learn to live in love
and in His kingdom share.

2 He sent His Son, Lord Jesus Christ,
to show His love for all,
and many people followed Christ
in answer to His call.

3 As God spoke then to men of old,
so still He speaks today,
we pray that we may learn His will
and follow in His way.

163 The children sang to Jesus

Mary A. Barbour
Capo 3

Phil Burt

The chil-dren sang to Je-sus, as He rode a - long. They
waved and waved their palm leaves while they sang this song;___ Ho - san - na! Ho-
san - na! Praise the King!___ Ho-san - na! Ho-san - na! Praise the King!

The children sang to Jesus,
as He rode along.
They waved and waved their palm leaves
while they sang this song;
Hosanna! Hosanna! Praise the King!
Hosanna! Hosanna! Praise the King!

164 The duck goes, 'Quack'

B.C. Hanson

Capo 1

1 The duck goes, 'Quack.' The duck goes, 'Quack.'
It swings across the yard and back.
The duck goes, 'Quack.' The duck goes, 'Quack.'
I'm glad that God made ducks.

2 The cow goes, 'Moo.' The cow goes, 'Moo.'
She gives good milk to me and you.
The cow goes, 'Moo.' The cow goes, 'Moo.'
I'm glad that God made cows.

3 The horse goes, 'Neigh.' The horse goes, 'Neigh.'
It likes to run and eat good hay.
The horse goes, 'Neigh.' The horse goes, 'Neigh.'
I'm glad God made the horse.

4 The cat goes, 'Purr.' The cat goes, 'Purr.'
I like to pet her soft warm fur.
The cat goes, 'Purr.' The cat goes, 'Purr.'
I'm glad that God made cats.

5 The dog can bark. The dog can bark.
It likes to run around the park.
The dog can bark. The dog can bark.
I'm glad that God made dogs.

165 The heavens are telling

Joan Robinson
arr. Phil Burt

The hea - vens are tell - ing the glo - ry of God;

each star and pla - net re - flects His love.

Look up and see how His power is dis - played.

His glo - ry we see in the things He has made.

Chorus

Je - sus is King Al - le - lu - ia! Je - sus is King Al - le - lu - ia!

Je - sus is King Al - le - lu - ia! Je - sus is King!

1 The heavens are telling
   the glory of God;
   each star and planet
   reflects His love.
   Look up and see how
   His power is displayed.
   His glory we see in the
   things He has made.
   Jesus is King Alleluia!
   Jesus is King Alleluia!
   Jesus is King. Alleluia!
   Jesus is King!

2 The sparrows are telling
   the glory of God;
   each bird and creature
   reflects His love.
   Look at yourself and see
   how His power is displayed.
   His glory we see
   in the things He has made.
   Jesus is . . .

3 The Cross it is telling
   the glory of God.
   Each awful nailprint
   reflects His love.
   Look at the empty tomb
   see His power displayed.
   His glory we see
   in the things He has made.
   Jesus is . . .

166 The Lord is my Shepherd

This song to be sung as a round

arr. Andy Silver

Capo 1

① F(E) ... C(B7) ... F(E)

The Lord is my Shep-herd, I'll trust in Him al-ways. He

C(B7) ... F(E) ②

leads me by still wa-ters, I'll trust in Him al-ways. Al-ways, al-ways, I'll

C(B7) ... F(E) ... C(B7) ... F(E)

trust in Him al-ways, al-ways, al-ways, I'll trust in Him al-ways.

* Alternative words the third line

1 The Lord is my Shepherd,
  I'll trust in Him always.
 *He leads me by still waters,
  I'll trust in Him always.
  Always, always, I'll trust in Him always,
  always, always, I'll trust in Him always.

2 He knows me and He loves me,

3 He gave His life to save me,

4 He's living now and helps me,

5 He cares for me and guides me,

6 He says, 'Fear not. I'm with you.'

167 These are written

Patricia Hetrick

These are written, that you might believe
that Jesus is the Christ, the Son of God.
These are written, that you might believe
that Jesus is the Christ, the Son of God.

168 There were one, two, three lepers

Romona Brown

There were one, (clap, clap, clap, clap) two, (clap similarly)

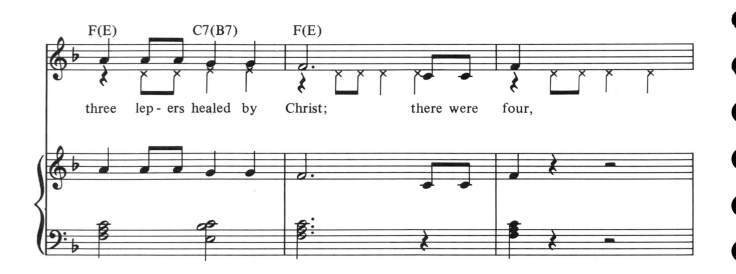

three lep - ers healed by Christ; there were four,

five, six lep - ers healed by Christ. There were

sev'n and eight and nine healed too. Ten in all were made brand new, but

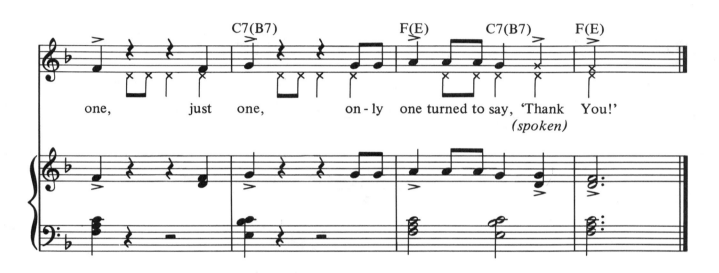

one, just one, on-ly one turned to say, 'Thank You!'
(spoken)

Suggested rhythm ♫ ♩ ♩

There were one, (clap, clap, clap, clap)
two, (clap, clap, clap, clap)
three lepers healed by Christ:
there were four, five,
six lepers healed by Christ.
There were seven and eight and nine healed too.
Ten in all were made brand new,
but one, just one, only one turned to say,
'Thank You'
(spoken)

169 The shepherds loved dear Jesus

arr. Phil Burt

The shep-herds loved dear Je-sus, they left their slee-ping sheep, and hurri-ed to the man-ger where Je-sus was a-sleep.

1 The shepherds loved dear Jesus,[1]
  they left their sleeping sheep,[2]
  and hurried to the manger[3]
  where Jesus was asleep.[4]

2 The shepherds loved dear Jesus,[1]
  they prayed to God and said,[5]
  'Thank You, God, for Jesus[5]
  In His manger bed.'[4]

3 The wise men loved dear Jesus[1]
  they followed God's bright star,[6]
  It led them to our best friend.
  They travelled from afar.

4 The wise men loved dear Jesus,[1]
  they brought to Him rich gifts,
  and thanked the Heavenly Father,[5]
  for His special gift.

1 Pretend to cradle baby in arms
2 Begin to walk fingers up arm
3 Walk fingers faster
4 Pillow head on hands
5 Fold hands in prayer
6 Walk pointing to 'star'

170 The shepherds were excited

Phil Burt

1 The shepherds were excited
   to hear the angel say,
   'You'll find the Babe in swaddling clothes
   in a manger bed of hay!

2 They ran as fast as they could go
   'twas as the angel said,
   for there were Joseph and Mary
   and God's Son in His manger bed.

3 How glad they were to see Him!
   They thanked God for His Son.
   Then hurried home to tell the news
   that God's own Son had come.

171 The wise man built his house upon the rock

arr. Phil Burt

rain came down and the floods came up,___ the rain came down and the floods came up, and the house on the rock stood firm.___

The wise man built his house upon the rock.
The wise man built his house upon the rock.
The wise man built his house upon the rock
and the rain came tumbling down.
And the rain came down and the floods came up,
the rain came down and the floods came up,
the rain came down and the floods came up,
and the house on the rock stood firm.

The foolish man built his house upon the sand.
The foolish man built his house upon the sand.
The foolish man built his house upon the sand
and the rain came tumbling down.
And the rain came down and the floods came up,
the rain came down and the floods came up,
the rain came down and the floods came up,
and the house on the sand fell flat.

172 This is the day

Les Garret
arr. Phil Burt

This is___ the day, this is___ the day that the
Lord has made, that the Lord has made. We will___ re-joice,
we will___ re-joice and be glad in it, and be glad in it.
This is___ the day that the Lord has___ made,

This is the day,
this is the day that the Lord has made,
that the Lord has made.
We will rejoice,
we will rejoice and be glad in it,
and be glad in it.
This is the day that the Lord has made,
we will rejoice and be glad in it.
This is the day,
this is the day that the Lord has made.

173 This little light of mine

shine my light both bright and clear._ Where there's a dark cor-ner

in this land_ I'm gon-na let my lit-tle light shine.

This little light of mine, I'm gonna let it shine.
This little light of mine, I'm gonna let it shine.
This little light of mine, I'm gonna let it shine;
let it shine, let it shine, let it shine.

1 The light that shines is the light of love,
   lights the darkness from above.
   It shines on me and it shines on you,
   and shows what the power of love can do.
   I'm gonna shine my light both far and near,
   I'm gonna shine my light both bright and clear.
   Where there's a dark corner in this land
   I'm gonna let my little light shine.
      This little light of mine . . .

2 On Monday He gave me the gift of love,
   Tuesday, peace came from above.
   On Wednesday He told me to have more faith,
   on Thursday He gave me a little more grace.
   Friday, He told me just to watch and pray,
   Saturday, He told me just what to say.
   On Sunday He gave me the power divine
   to let my little light shine.
      This little light of mine . . .

174 This is how Dorcas sewed a dress

Traditional
arr. Phil Burt

1 This is how Dorcas sewed a dress,
   sewed a dress, sewed a dress.
   This is how Dorcas sewed a dress
   to share with other people.

   (made some soup, made some bread)

2 This is how Martha baked a cake,
   baked a cake, baked a cake.
   This is how Martha baked a cake,
   when Jesus came to visit.

   (dusted the room, sat at His feet, swept
   the floor, set the table)

175 Three ladies are walking

Phil Burt

Three ladies are walking along, sad as they can be. Jesus was their dearest friend, and He was dead, you see. But when they came to where He lay they stopped with great surprise! For the

Three ladies are walking along
sad as they can be.
Jesus was their dearest Friend
and He was dead, you see.
But when they came to where He lay
they stopped with great surprise!
For the great big stone was rolled away
and two angels said,
'Jesus is not here! He's alive!
Jesus is not here! He's alive!
Jesus is not here! He's alive!'

176 Two little eyes

C.C. Kerr

Two little eyes to look to God,
two little ears to hear His Word,
two little feet to walk in His ways,
two little lips to sing His praise,
two little hands to do His will,
and one little heart to love Him still.

177 Up the mountain

(Based on Exodus 19:1-20; 20:1-21; 32:15-16)

Traditional
arr. Phil Burt

1 Up the mountain Moses walked, Moses walked,
Moses walked.
  (Walk in a circle as if climbing a mountain.)
Up the mountain Moses walked,
  (Keep walking.)
to talk to the Lord.
  *(Open and close hand to simulate talking;
  then point toward heaven.)*

In successive stanzas use:

2 This is the way the people washed,
  (Scrub clothes in a basin; wash faces, hands, etc.)
before they heard the Lord.
  (Cup hand up to ear; point toward heaven.)

3 This is the way the thunder crashed,
  (Clap hands when 'thunder' is sung.)
they knew it was the Lord.
  (Nod head and point toward heaven.)

4 This is the way Moses carried the stones,
  (Walk in circle with hands outstretched, palms up.)
God's holy Word.
  *(With one hand still carrying the stones,
  point with other hand upward, then to the palm of
  the outstretched hand.)*

178 Wandering like a lost sheep

Andy Silver

Wan - der - ing like lost sheep we're go - ing our own way, when

Je - sus the good Shep - herd found us, led us home, laid

down His life be - fore us that we might all be saved. We

now be - long to Je - sus, we now be - long to Him.

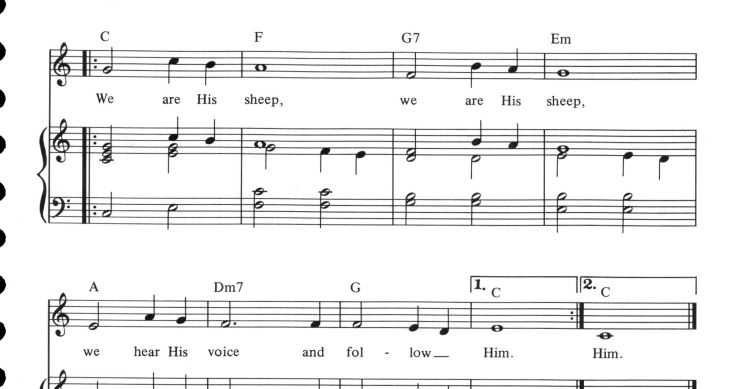

We are His sheep, we are His sheep,
we hear His voice and fol - low — Him. Him.

Wandering like lost sheep we're going our own way,
when Jesus the good Shepherd found us, led us home,
laid down His life before us that we might all be saved.
We now belong to Jesus, we now belong to Him.
We are His sheep, we are His sheep,
we hear His voice, and follow Him.
We are His sheep, we are His sheep,
we hear His voice and follow Him.

179 We are soldiers of the King

Greg Leavers
arr. Phil Burt

We are sol-diers of the King, of His vic-tory we will sing. Liv - ing ev - 'ry hour, by the Spir - it's power, mar - ching in the name of Je - sus. Enemies are all a -

We are soldiers of the King,
of His victory we will sing.
Living every hour by the Spirit's power,
marching in the Name of Jesus.
Enemies are all around,
as we praise they're losing ground.
Trusting in God's Word, it's a mighty sword,
forever friendly, faithful followers fighting for the King.

180 We have a king who rides a donkey

Fred Kaan
Capo 5

Traditional
arr. Phil Burt

We have a king who rides a don-key, we have a king who rides a don-key,

we have a king who rides a don-key and His name is Je - sus.

Je - sus, the King, is ris - en, Je - sus, the King, is ris - en,

Je - sus, the King, is ris - en, ear - ly in the morn - ing.

1 We have a king who rides a donkey,
  we have a king who rides a donkey,
  we have a king who rides a donkey
  and His name is Jesus.

  Jesus, the King, is risen,
  Jesus, the King, is risen,
  Jesus, the King, is risen,
  Early in the morning.

2 Trees are waving a royal welcome,
  trees are waving a royal welcome,
  trees are waving a royal welcome
  for the King called Jesus.
  Jesus, the King, is risen . . .

3 We have a king who cares for people,
  we have a king who cares for people,
  we have a king who cares for people
  and His name is Jesus.
  Jesus, the King, is risen . . .

4 What shall we do with our life this morning?
  What shall we do with our life this morning?
  What shall we do with our life this morning?
  Give it up in service!
  Jesus, the King, is risen . . .

181 We have some news to bring

Greg Leavers
arr. Phil Burt

We have some news to bring— and so this song we'll sing,— that a Babe's been born— who is a hea - ven - ly king.— And the mess - age we bring— is that Christ - mas is for Him. It's a birth day ce - leb - ra - tion for a King.

We have some news to bring
and so this song we'll sing,
that a babe's been born
who is a heavenly King.
And the message we bring
is that Christmas is for Him.
It's a birthday celebration for a King.

1 Jesus was born in a stable,
   the angels spread the joyful news,
   the angels spread the joyful news.
   NOW WE CAN SING IT AGAIN!
   We have some news . . .

2 Shepherds came down from the hillside
   to worship Christ, the newborn King,
   to worship Christ, the newborn King.
   NOW WE CAN SING IT AGAIN!
   We have some news . . .

3 A star led wise men to Jesus,
   they brought gold, frankincense and myrrh,
   they brought gold, frankincense and myrrh.
   NOW WE CAN SING IT AGAIN!
   We have some news . . .

182 We praise You for Your love

Alice M. Pullen

G. Paisallo

Capo 1

We praise You for Your love,
our friend and Father God,
who gives us healing, strength and joy,
we praise You for Your love.

183 We thank You Father

Anon
arr. Phil Burt

We thank You Father for today
and all the work we've done,
for help we have been given,
for our learning and our fun.

184 We're sailing over the sea so deep

Greg Leavers
arr. Phil Burt

We're sail - ing o - ver the sea so deep but shhh! for Je - sus is fast a sleep. Now look a sto - rm is all a - round, the wind and the waves throw us up and down. I'm feel - ing so frigh - tened, quick Je - sus please

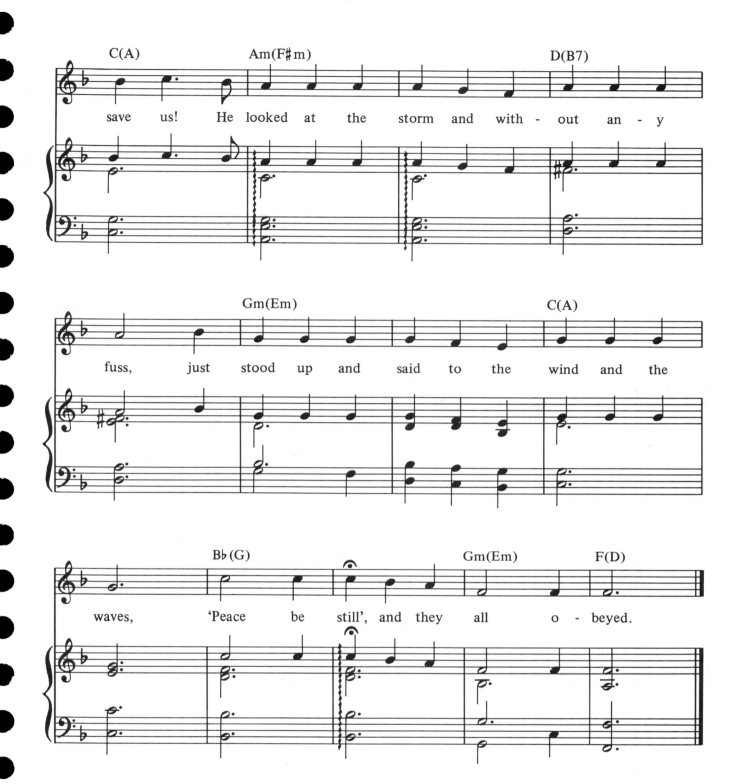

We're sailing over the sea so deep
but shhh! for Jesus is fast asleep.
Now look a storm is all around,
the wind and the waves throw us up and down.
I'm feeling so frightened, quick Jesus please save us!
He looked at the storm and without any fuss,
just stood up and said to the wind and the waves,
'Peace be still', and they all obeyed.

185 What a wonderful Saviour is Jesus

arr. Phil Burt

What a won-der-ful Sav-iour is Je-sus,— what a won-der-ful Friend is He, for He left all the glo-ry of hea-ven,— came to earth to die on Cal-va-ry: Sing Ho-san-na! Sing Ho-san-na! Sing Ho-san-na to the King of kings!

arr. © 1988 Phil Burt

Sing Ho-san - na! Sing Ho-san - na! Sing Ho-san-na to the King.

1 What a wonderful Saviour is Jesus,
   what a wonderful Friend is He,
   for He left all the glory of heaven,
   came to earth to die on Calvary:

   Sing Hosanna! Sing Hosanna!
   Sing Hosanna! to the King of kings!
   Sing Hosanna! Sing Hosanna!
   Sing Hosanna to the King.

2 He arose from the grave, Hallelujah,
   and He lives never more to die,
   at the Father's right hand interceding,
   He will hear and heed our faintest cry:
   Sing Hosanna! . . .

3 He is coming some day to receive us,
   we'll be caught up to heaven above,
   what a joy it will be to behold Him,
   sing forever of His grace and love:
      Sing Hosanna! . . .

186 What shall we do?

Marie H. Frost

Anon
arr. Phil Burt

What shall we do when we help to-day? Help to-day, help to-day. what shall we do when we help to-day? Help to please our Lord.

1 What shall we do when we help today?
Help today, help today.
What shall we do when we help today?
Help to please our Lord.

2 We will help and sweep the floor,
sweep the floor, sweep the floor.
We will help and sweep the floor,
help to please our Lord.

3 We will put the books away,
books away, books away.
We will put the books away,
help to please our Lord.

4 We will pick up toys today,
pick up toys, pick up toys.
We will pick up toys today,
help to please our Lord.

5 We will dust the room today,
dust the room, dust the room.
We will dust the room today,
help to please our Lord.

187 When God breathes

Joan Robinson
arr. Phil Burt

1 When God breathes 2 His Spirit 3 in my life,
1 when God breathes 2 His Spirit 3 in my life,
1 when God breathes 2 His Spirit 3 in my life,
4 then I will shine, shine for Him.

Actions 1 *Hands cupped to blow*   3 *Hands on chest*
2 *Arms stretched up*   4 *Arms waved from side to side*

188 What wonderful things

Peter Lewis

What won-der-ful things are arms,_____ what
won-der-ful things are legs,_____ how
won-der-f'ly God has made us all, He gave us our
bo-dies and heads.____ What love.____

All but last time What
Last time love.

1 What wonderful things are arms,
  what wonderful things are legs,
  how wonderfuly God has made me, for
  He gave me my body and head.

2 What wonderful things are hands,
  what wonderful things are feet,
  how wonderfuly God has made me, for
  He gave me my hair and my teath.

3 What wonderful things are fingers,
  what wonderful things are toes,
  how wonderfuly God has made me, for
  He gave me my chin and my nose.

4 What wonderful things are ears,
  what wonderful things are eyes,
  how wonderfuly God has made me, for
  He gave me my shape and my size.

5 How wonderful we can think,
  how wonderful we can move,
  how wonderfuly God has made me, for
  He gave me my life with His love.

EXTRA VERSE IF WANTED

What wonderful things are mouths,
what wonderful things are tongues,
how wonderfuly God has made us all,
He gave us our hearts and our lungs.

189 When I go to the animal zoo

Susan E. Payne

Ellen R. Thompson
arr. Phil Burt

When I go to the a-ni-mal zoo, I can see what God can do, God can do. He can make a_ el-eph-ant BIG. *(Walk like an elephant.)* He can make a kan-ga-roo HOP. *(Hop.)*

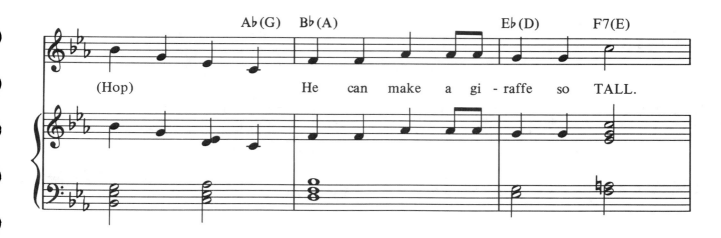

Ab(G) Bb(A) Eb(D) F7(E)

(Hop) He can make a gi - raffe so TALL.

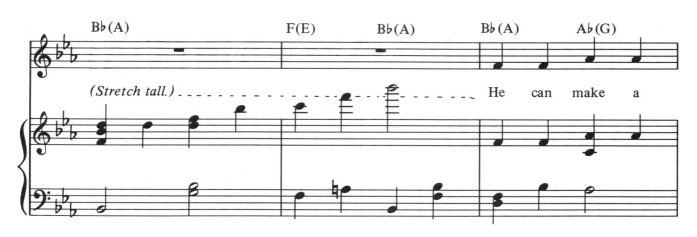

Bb(A) F(E) Bb(A) Bb(A) Ab(G)

(Stretch tall.) - - - - - - - - - - - - - - - He can make a

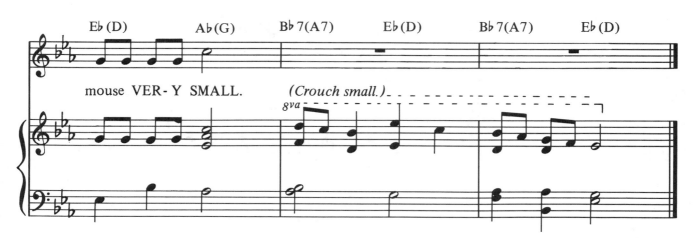

Eb(D) Ab(G) Bb7(A7) Eb(D) Bb7(A7) Eb(D)

mouse VER- Y SMALL. (Crouch small.) - - - - - - - - - - - - - - - - -
8va -

When I go to the animal zoo,
I can see what God can do.

He can make an elephant BIG.   *(Walk like an elephant)*
He can make a kangaroo HOP.   *(Hop)*
He can make a giraffe so TALL.   *(Stretch tall)*
He can make a mouse VERY SMALL. *(Crouch small)*
When I go . . .

He can make a lion ROAR.   *(Roar)*
He can make a monkey CLIMB.   *(Make climbing motions)*
He can make a little bird FLY.   *(Pretend to fly)*
He can make a fishywishy SWIM. *(Make hands swim like a fish)*
When I go.. . .

190 When I'm feeling lonely

Greg Leavers

Capo 2

When I'm fee - ling lone - ly, _____ when I'm fee - ling blue,

when I'm fee - ling so fed up, I can al - ways talk to You.

Lord, _____ You hear me when I pray,

Lord, _____ You're near me ev -'ry day.

When I'm feeling lonely, when I'm feeling blue,
when I'm feeling so fed up, I can always talk to You.
Lord, You hear me when I pray,
Lord, You're near me every day.
Thank You Lord, You always see me through,
I'll never, ever, find a friend as good as You.
I'll never, ever, find a friend as good as You.

191 When no one else

Mary Le Bar

Harry Dixon Loes

Capo 3

1. When no one else could make the girl live, Je - sus could! Je - sus could! He's God's dear Son, who shows to us all that God is good, God is good.

1 When no one else could make the girl live,
Jesus could! Jesus could!
He's God's dear Son, who shows to us all
that God is good, God is good.

2 When no one else could make the man well,
Jesus could! Jesus could!
He's God's dear Son, who shows to us all
that God is good, God is good.

3 When no one else could stop the wild storm,
Jesus could! Jesus could!
He's God's dear Son, who shows to us all
that God is good, God is good.

* Teach each stanza only after the children have heard the Bible story of which it speaks.
   (1. Mark 5:21-43:2. Mark 2:1-12:3. Mark 4:35-41)

192 When the rain falls

Joan Robinson
arr. Phil Burt

1 When the rain falls down on my head
I shout thank you, I shout thank-you.
When the rain falls down on my head
I shout thank You Lord for the rain.

2 When the rain makes the puddles I love
I shout thank You, I shout thank-you.
When the rain makes the puddles I love
I shout thank You Lord for the rain.

3 When the rain makes the flowers to grow
I shout thank you, I shout thank-you.
When the rain makes the flowers to grow
I shout thank You Lord for the rain.

4 The rain makes me think of You
I shout thank You, I shout thank-you.
The rain makes me think of You
I shout thank You Lord for the rain.

193 When we look up

Andy Silver

When we look up to the sky
and we see the sparrows fly,
let's remember that Jesus knows them all.
When we see the lovely trees
and the flowers and the leaves,
let's remember that Jesus made them all.
J.E.S.U.S. C.A.R.E.S.
Jesus cares for all the things He made,
that means you and me,
our friends and family.
Thank You Jesus for caring for me.

194 When you're in a jam

Joan Robinson
arr. Phil Burt

When you're in a jam
just stop and pray.
Let Jesus tell you
what to do and say.
When you're in a jam
just call on Him
and He will help you
to do the right thing.

195 Who made the twinkling stars?

Anon
arr. Phil Burt

Who made the twink-ling stars, the twink-ling stars, the twink-ling stars?

Who made the twink-ling stars? Our Fa-ther God.

1 Who made the twinkling stars,
the twinkling stars, the twinkling stars?
Who made the twinkling stars?
Our Father God.

2 Who made the birds that fly,
the birds that fly, the birds that fly?
Who made the birds that fly?
Our Father God.

3 Who made the rolling seas,
the rolling seas, the rolling seas?
Who made the rolling seas?
Our Father God.

4 Who made you and me,
you and me, you and me?
Who made you and me?
Our Father God.

196 Whether you're one

Graham Kendrick
arr. Phil Burt

Whether you're one or whether you're two or three or four or five, six or seven or eight or nine, it's good to be a - live. It real - ly does - n't mat - ter how old you are, Je - sus loves you who - ev - er you are.

La la la la la la la la la —— Je-sus loves us all.

La la la la la la la la la —— Je-sus loves us all.

1 Whether you're one or whether you're two
  or three or four or five,
  six or seven or eight or nine
  It's good to be alive.
  It really doesn't matter how old you are,
  Jesus loves you whoever you are.

  La la la la la la la la la
  Jesus loves us all.
  La la la la la la la la la
  Jesus loves us all.

2 Whether you're big or whether you're small
  or somewhere in between,
  first in the class or middle or last
  we're all the same to Him.
  It really doesn't matter how clever you are,
  Jesus loves you whoever you are.
    La la la la la la . . .

197 Who's the Babe?

Greg Leavers

Who's the __ Babe who made __ the an - gels __ sing?

Made the __ shep-herds want __ to wor - ship __ Him?

Made each __ wise man bring __ an of - fer - ing? _____ It's

Je - sus __ Christ the __ new - born __ King! So __

Who's the Babe who made the angels sing?
Made the shepherds want to worship Him?
Made each wise man bring an offering?
It's Jesus Chirst the new-born King!
So we sing glory, Halelujah,
a special thank you to our Saviour,
and so this Christmas, at the centre
we worship Jesus, the new born King.

198 Wide, wide as the ocean

C. Austin Miles

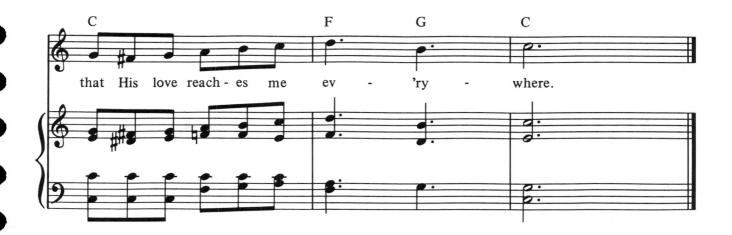

that His love reach - es me ev - 'ry - where.

Wide, wide as the ocean, high as the heaven above;
deep, deep as the deepest sea is my Saviour's love.
I, though so unworthy, still am a child of His care;
for His Word teaches me that His love reaches me everywhere.

199 With Jesus in the boat

arr. Phil Burt

With Je-sus in the boat we can smile at the storm, smile at the storm, smile at the storm. With Je-sus in the boat we can smile at the storm as we go sail-ing home. Sail - ing, sail - ing home, sail - ing,

sail - ing home, with Je - sus in the boat we can

smile at the storm as we go sail - ing home.

With Jesus in the boat we can smile at the storm,
smile at the storm, smile at the storm.
With Jesus is the boat we can smile at the storm
as we go sailing home.
Sailing, sailing home,
sailing, sailing home.
With Jesus is the boat we can smile at the storm
as we go sailing home.

200 You are holy

Greg Leavers

You are ho - ly, _____ so You hate all we do

wrong. You are lo - ving, _____ for our sin You gave Your

Son. You are Fa - ther, _____ the great pro - tec - tor, _____

_____ You are migh - ty, _____ the great Cre - a - tor, _____

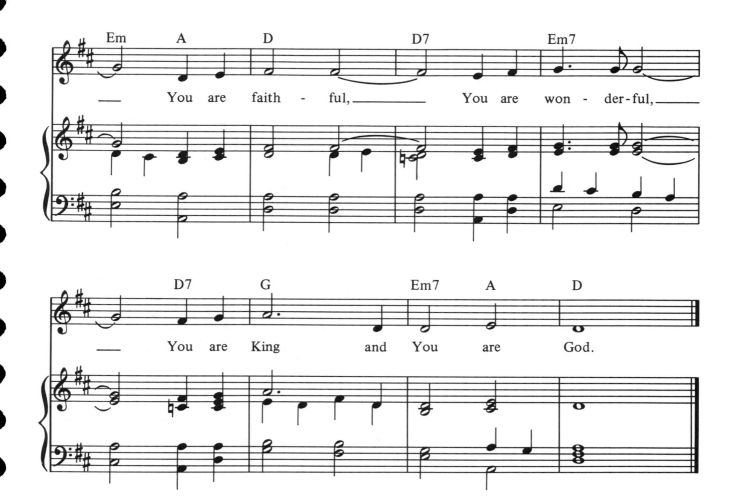

You are holy, so You hate all we do wrong.
You are loving, for our sin You gave Your Son.
You are Father, the great protector,
You are mighty, the great Creator,
You are faithful, You are wonderful,
You are King and You are God.

201 You're my maker

Joan Robinson
arr. Phil Burt

G   **Am**

1. You're my mak - er, You're my mu - sic, You're the mas - ter of my

D7   **Am**   **D7**

life. You're my ma - ker, You're my mu - sic, You're the mas - ter of my

G   **D7**   **G**   **Am**

life. You're my mak - er, You're my mu - sic, You're the mas - ter of my

D   **C**   **D**   **G**

life, and I love you Je - sus my Lord._____

1 You're my maker, You're my music,
You're the master of my life.
You're my maker, You're my music,
You're the master of my life.
You're my maker, You're my music,
You're the master of my life,
and I love You Jesus my Lord.

2 You're the sunshine and the sweetness,
You're the Saviour of my soul.
You're the sunshine and the sweetness,
You're the Saviour of my soul.
You're the sunshine and the sweetness,
You're the Saviour of my soul,
and I love You Jesus my King.

3 You're the ruler and the richness,
the Redeemer of my life.
You're the ruler and the richness,
the Redeemer of my life.
You're the ruler and the richness,
the Redeemer of my life,
and I love You Jesus my King.

202 Zacchaeus was a very little man

Luke 19:4

Anon
arr. J.W.

Zac - chae - us was a ve - ry lit - tle man, and a ve - ry lit - tle man was he. He climbed up in - to a sy - ca - more tree, for the Sa - viour he wan - ted to see. And when the Sa - viour passed that way, He

Zacchaeus was a very little man,
and a very little man was he.
He climbed up into a sycamore tree,
for the Saviour he wanted to see.
And when the Saviour passed that way,
He looked into the tree and said,
'Now, Zacchaeus, you come down,
for I'm coming to your house to tea.'

203 Who made your eyes?

Lillian Waldecker

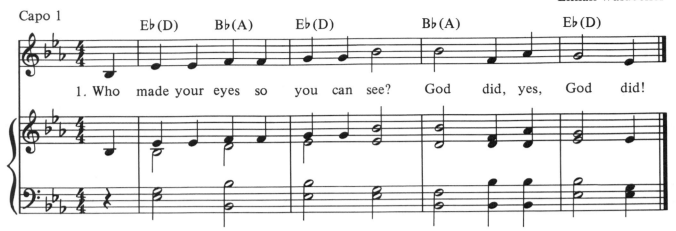

Capo 1

Actions:

Point to each member of the body as it is mentioned.
Point upward on the words, 'God did.'

1 Who made your eyes so you can see?
   God did, yes, God did!

2 Who made your ears so you can hear?
   God did, yes, God did!

3 Who made your tongue so you can speak?
   God did, yes, God did!

4 Who made your hands so you can work?
   God did, yes, God did!

5 Who made your feet so you can walk?
   God did, yes, God did!

Chord Chart

Using the Chord Chart

This chart contains all the chords you will need to play all the hymns and songs in this book. Even if a chord looks more difficult than those you are used to playing, DO TRY. Always seek to improve your knowledge and playing ability. It may seem to you that you have a very large number of chords to learn, but don't panic! For example, look at Fm, F♯m, Gm, and G♯m, and you will see that they all have the same finger formation, but are on different frets for each chord. So, if you learn the ONE finger formation, you can immediately play *four new chords!*

If you want to play chords in a different key to the one set (because, for example, of a limited chord knowledge) you can very simply use this chart to discover the chords you need. Here's how you do it:

1. Locate the key chord that is set in the original. Find it on the chart in the SECOND COLUMN for the *major* keys and the THIRD COLUMN for *minor* keys.
2. Locate on the chart the new key that you wish to play the music in (also in the second column for *major* keys and the third column for *minor* keys).
3. Work out the rest of the chords that need to be changed by noting their position around the original key chord and finding the chord that is *in exactly the same position* around the new key chord.

Example:

When changing from key chord F to key chord E, find F and E in the second column of the chart. On the left of F you will find C7. The equivalent chord in key E is therefore the one on the left of E, B7. Similarly Dm would become C♯m, and B♭ would become A.

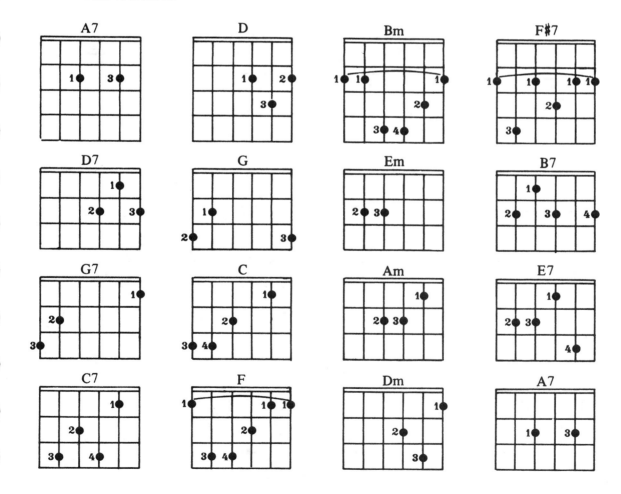

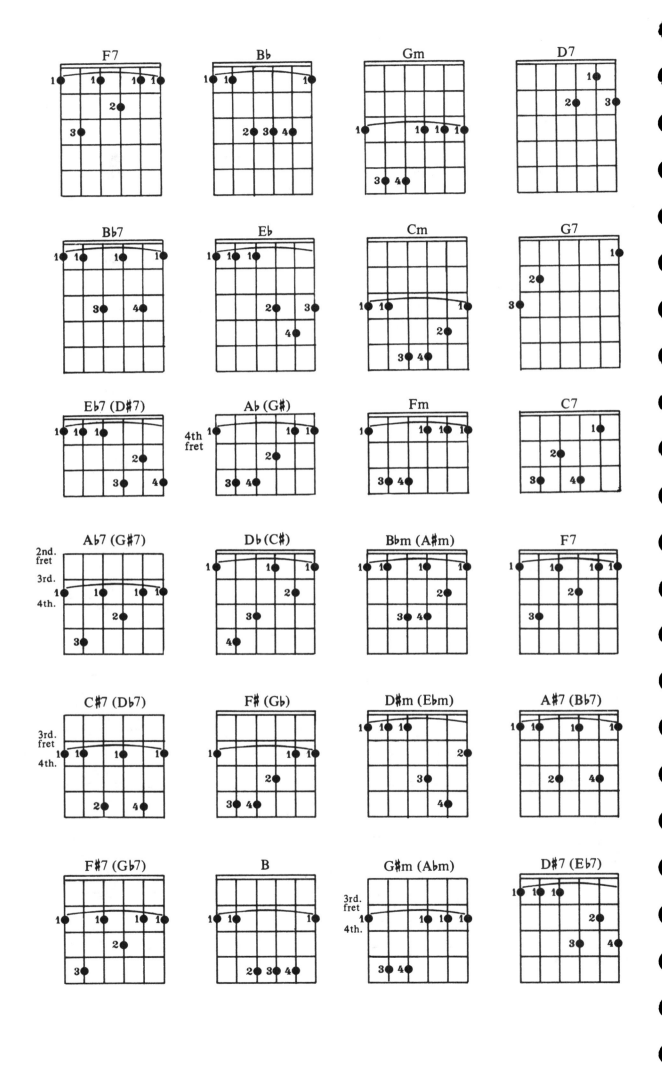

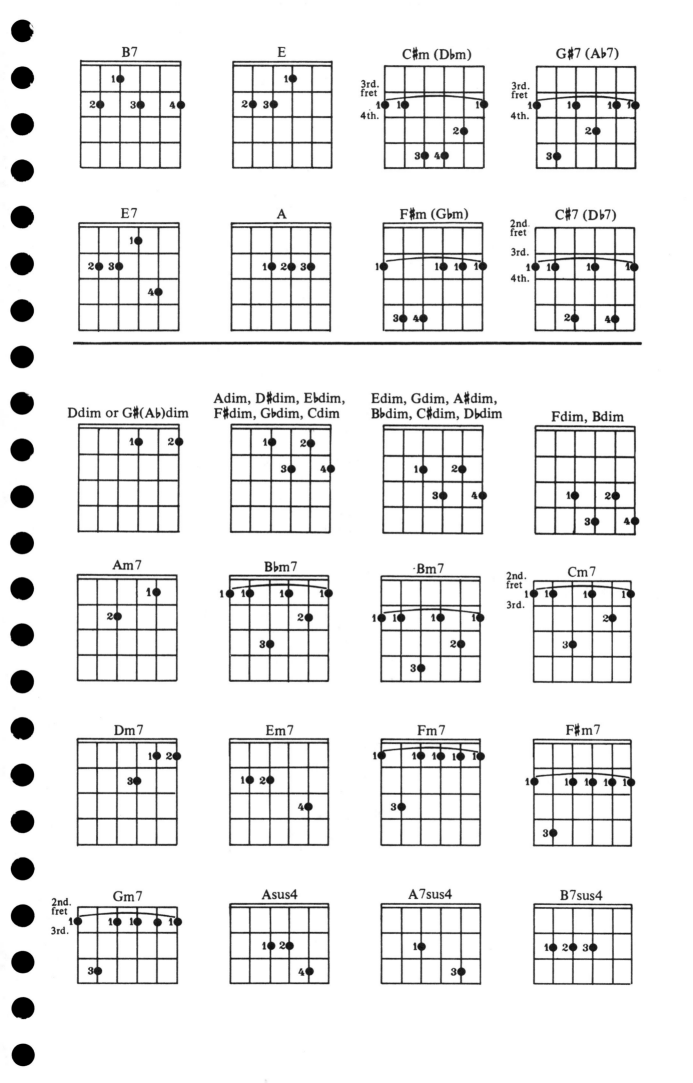

Subject index

Index of first lines and titles